HEROES
OF THE
GREEN AGE

—

Heroes of the Green Age
The Men, Women and Ideas
Shaping Our Low Carbon Future — and Why
We Cannot Afford to Let Them Down
By Erik Rasmussen and Per Meilstrup

© 2009 Erik Rasmussen and Per Meilstrup, and
Lindhardt and Ringhof A/S
Photos ©
Our sincere thanks to the contributing
innovators and the companies for providing
illustrations.

Editor-in-chief: Lone Fredensborg
Editor Illustrations: Conny Mikkelsen
Chief sub-editor: Stine Dahlgren
Translation from Danish to English:
James Bulman-May, From High Tech to Green
Tech by Justin Gerdes.
Illustrations: Rasmus Buhl
Design and cover: daddy
The book is set in stag by daddy and printed
by Livonia Print.

ISBN 978-87-1142-643-2
1st edition

Printed in Latvia

Photo copyright:
Polfoto, Corbis, Getty Images, and Scanpix.
"Smoke": page 145, photos by
Søren Springborg.
"Welcome to Climateville": page 53,
Patrick Blanc, Vertical Garden.
"The Innovator from Samsø", page 111,
Joachim Ladefoged.
"The Design Hippie", page 176, Mikkel Andersen
Mayday Press.

The book is printed on FSC-classified paper
(Forest Stewardship Council), which means
that it comes from sustainable forests.

www.lindhardtogringhof.dk

Lindhardt and Ringhof A/S ,
an Egmont company.

HEROES
OF THE
GREEN AGE

—

The **MEN**, **WOMEN** and **IDEAS**
Shaping Our Low Carbon Future – and Why
We Cannot Afford to Let Them Down
By
Erik Rasmussen & **Per Meilstrup**

—

Planning and editing: Lene Møller Jørgensen

Contributions by Lea Klæstrup Andersen, Justin Gerdes, Christian Korsgaard,
Karin Lohmann, Helle Maj, Mikkel Andersen, Mette Hjermind McCall,
Helge Pedersen, Charlotte Sylvestersen and Lone Theils.

CONTENTS

—

—

The medium height, dark man turns to me. The brown eyes are radiant. He is in his mid-forties, dressed in an expensive, tight fitting suit, a white shirt, and a blue silk tie. He is a perfect example of an up and coming businessman from Silicon Valley. He has raised 1 billion dollars as seed money for the project which he is in town to present. However, it is not IT that makes Shai Agassi's eyes sparkle. It is cars. Electric cars that run on renewable solar or wind energy. **"We link a system of cars to a wind turbine park. Your car will be running on clean electrons. It will be faster than an ordinary car and take less time to accelerate. It is also completely silent,"** he explains with a smile.

—

THE NEXT GIANT LEAP FOR MANKIND

—

Try to cast your mind twenty years back in time to the end of the 1980s. This was the time when the Berlin Wall fell, George Bush senior moved into the White House, and the Romanian dictator Nicolai Ceausescu's regime was toppled, and he was executed on a Christmas morning in Târgovişte. Around this time the Harry Potter actor Daniel Radcliffe was born and the world sang along to Michael Jackson's *Bad*.

Now make a mental list of the things you did not have then. Products, appliances, and goods that did not yet exist. For example sphygmometers, halogen bulbs, laser dentist's drills, the Internet, HIV medication, MP3 players, airbags, e-mails, DAB radios, flat screens, charter trips to Thailand, shock absorbing running shoes, chip cards, viagra, GPS, insulin pens, GoogleEarth, micro loans, automatic traffic information on the car radio, lights

that switch themselves off when the room is empty, and taps that turn on when you place your hand underneath them. The list goes on indefinitely. In just two decades innovation has changed the world and our daily lives almost beyond recognition.

Today we can entertain our children with bizarre stories about the past: just a few years ago we had to get up from the couch every time we wanted to change television chan-

"

AS CREATIVE ENTREPRENEURS TURN THEIR MINDS TO THE CHALLENGES POSED BY A LOW CARBON ECONOMY, THE EXCITEMENT AND DRIVE OF INNOVATION IS EVIDENT. THIS CAN BE THE SPUR TO REAL GROWTH THAT HAS SO LONG BEEN MISSING.

"

Nobel Prize winner **Joseph Stieglitz** and climate economist **Lord Nicholas Stern**

—

nels. Back then we had mobile telephones the size of espresso machines, and we went to the post office to dispatch telegrams in weird staccato codes. In those days we could not predict how innovation would change the world. Of course we knew that the television manufacturers continually attempted to make smarter televisions, and that researchers worldwide attempted to develop AIDS medication. But. Micro loans? MP3 players? The inventions have arrived on our doorstep in such intricate and inscrutable ways that we had no chance of predicting them. Twenty years ago who would have been able to imagine GoogleEarth as a free global service? Or Viagra?

Humanity's innovative abilities are surprising and impressive and go far beyond our imaginative scope. Under the right circumstances an innovation year can be like a dog's year – seven times as long as a human year – said

Vint Cerf, one of the Google philosophers, when the dotcom wave peaked.

When discussing global warming, the years 2020, 2030, and 2050 constantly pop up, as do the goals we must have achieved by those dates with respect to CO_2 emission, the ratio of renewable energy, the development of battery technology, etc. We talk so much about it and with such serious demeanor that we forget that it is all guesswork. We have no idea what the world will look like, and certainly not what technologies we will have at our disposal in 10, 20 and 40 years. In 1989 we did not know what the world would look like in 2009 and our clairvoyant abilities have probably not improved since then. However, one thing we do know is that the great ideas and paradigm shifts occur during the major crises. It is in times of famine, poverty and war that the best innovations are made. This is when the drive and the dynamism, which Stieglitz and Stern

mention in the epigraph, bloom. Europe's greatest leap in growth took place in the ruins of two world wars, American society was created by hungry emigrants, and the Renaissance occurred in the wake of the Dark Ages.

Global warming is to the contemporary world what civilizational collapse, plagues, and world wars were to our ancestors. Not only will it have serious consequences for nature, it will also affect our economy, our way of life, and our society. It is a fundamental, global crisis, which already today affects many people and it shows no mercy. Those who have contributed the least to the problem are those who will be affected the most. In a few years we will all feel it. Your city, your home, your job, your car, your electricity bill, and your bank account will be influenced by it and most likely in negative ways.

There is reason to believe that we are again facing a threat that will bring out the best in us. And it is about time. If we do not change our ways the consequences will be catastrophic in the worst sense of the word. Not necessarily for the planet, but for the human race. "Nature will be OK," says James Lovelock, the British scientist who developed the famous Gaia theory about the planet as a self-regulating, ecological system. "The human race has a problem," he says. According to Lovelock, the planet will always remove the source of the imbalance "like a cancer tumor". And in this case the cancerous tumor is us, the human race. We will soon have more than 6 billion human beings on the planet and it will become increasingly difficult for us to sustain ourselves. Even more so when in the next decades our number will increase to 9 billion people. The scientist, the Nobel Prize winner Steven Chu, who is presently Secretary of Energy in Obama's government, describes the situation differently: "Earth will become an unknown place for the human race." Our home through tens of thousands of years will in the next decades undergo fundamental changes to the extent that we will not be able to recognize it. Even the world map itself will be altered, the shape of the continents, the sea currents, the ice caps, the forests.

However, this book is not about the climate problem. It is about the climate solutions and the ideas of today that will shape the world of tomorrow. Global warming is manmade – and so are the solutions to control it. One could be tempted to say that this is obvious. At this very moment thousands of innovators and entrepreneurs around the world are creating surprising, efficient, impressive, and daring methods to reduce the emissions. This book focuses on the men and women who are

building our common future. Their stories are inspiring, fascinating, and at times also entertaining. They are intelligent and deeply committed people. However, they are also dedicated nerds who have a manic insistence that we should take their ideas seriously along with the spark of madness that is sometimes necessary to ignite the tinderbox of innovation. We need their drive and ideas to solve the climate crisis. We must get to know them since they are the ones who will secure our future. And we have every reason to guarantee them conditions which will encourage them and reward their efforts.

Strangely enough we rarely hear about them. Newspaper articles and documentaries about climate change usually revolve around politics and science, suits, ties, floods and melting glaciers. Political summits and natural disasters go hand in glove with the traditional genres of journalism. In addition, climate experts have developed a coded language for insiders that makes it difficult for others to understand and engage with the climate problem.

We believe that the stories on the following pages deal with the real issues. Whether they relate the stories of the Decaux brothers from France, who put thousands of bikes at the disposal of the public in all the European metropolises, the inventor who generates renewable energy from kites in space, the pioneer who dreams of cars running on sun and wind energy, or the entrepreneur who transforms waste into to fuel in African villages.

The following pages record a journey in search of the next giant leap of mankind. From the high tech of Silicon Valley in California and Hong Kong's stressful business circles to the green hills of Nicaragua, the villages

in Uganda, and the 100 percent CO_2 neutral Danish island of Samsø. It is a turbulent and moving trip round the planet. We meet men and women full of drive and confidence in the future. We document that mankind is on the threshold of an innovation boom, an industrial revolution. Green technology is changing our world and thereby preserving it for the coming generations. In this process the technologies will create new societies, new growth, and millions of new, green jobs.

If we want to, of course.

Presently the international community faces a choice. It is not a difficult choice, but a choice of great significance. Either we continue on our present course, where our economy is mainly based on what the American commentator Thomas L. Friedman calls "energy from hell", i.e. coal, oil, and gas that we extract from the ground. Or we choose "energy from heaven", i.e. renewable energy from wind, sun, and water. The first choice is associated with great risks. The second choice means that we as of today must engineer a supreme global effort in order to forward innovation in sustainable technologies.

If a newspaper article or a politician for one moment makes you believe that we have already chosen heaven over hell, then you are seriously mistaken. Today we have designed our society in such a way that we favor coal, oil, and gas at the expense of sun, wind, and water. The fossil fuels make up 80 percent of our cumulative energy consumption. They will continue to do so in the coming decades, till we run out (which we will around the time when your grandchildren or great grandchildren grow up). We are in need of basic structures that will incite and reward the use of non-polluting energy and punish the use of polluting energy. The green innovators in this book contribute with their inventions in spite of the rules and regulations of society.

This book shows that we are letting the green innovators down, even though we are profoundly dependent on them. In so doing, we are in many ways digging our own grave. Without thousands of green ideas we will destroy our future.

In this book we dare to draw attention to some people at the expense of others. For this reason we would like to emphasize that we portray these people as examples. Brilliant examples of brains who have committed themselves to developing ideas that can save the world. Ideas that will hopefully lead by example.

The people in the book have been selected on the basis of a number of criteria:
■ Their innovation must be their own – or done in a team;
■ Their project must have the potential to influence the daily lives of many people in the coming decades; and
■ Their idea must be promising in terms of cutting down on the CO_2 emission, and it must have been tested successfully – either in the laboratory or on the market.

Furthermore it must be possible to label the idea as "climate innovation". That means that it must excel by being more climate friendly than a similar traditional solution. The EU among others applies the definition in questions of climate technology.

It has been important to us to focus on people, who actually make a difference and produce something. We have not included the many people who discuss the climate problem, since they are usually the ones who are featured in newspapers and television.

WHAT IS INNOVATION?
—
There are quite a few definitions of innovation, and some of them are very innovative. You find the simplest definition on Wikipedia: *The concept of innovation signifies a new way of doing something.* **More comprehensive definitions are applied by among others Copenhagen Business School:** *Innovation occurs when one attempts to solve real challenges and problems by applying technology and inventions, and combining the efforts with an understanding of how business works.* **It seems that innovation is more than a good idea. The good idea must also be realized – for example by being produced and marketed as a product that creates real change. However, a unique focus on technology is too narrow. Innovation can also encompass for instance processes and politics.**
—

Politicians, activists, and commentators are necessary when it comes to driving a new development. However, at the end of the day it is not Tony Blair, nor is it Greenpeace, nor for that matter two representatives from a Scandinavian think tank, who change the world. Those who invent and create goods, service functions or products in the real world deserve that honor.

Some of the green innovators in this book want to save the world. Others want to serve the local communities. Still others are motivated by making money. To us it makes no difference. All examples shine in the heavens of green innovation and the story of each and every innovator is important. If the Decaux brothers in France are driven by the need to sell advertisements, then that is splendid. Their concept has turned out to be efficient in the battle against one of the die-hard problems of the European metropolitan areas: to diminish car traffic and promote non-polluting transport. This exemplifies the fact that when the urge to innovate and do business walk hand in hand, then you can accomplish remarkable results.

The most important realization one can have, when reading about these wonderful, logical, and insane inventions, is that the climate society of the future is not all freezing temperatures, darkness and deprivation. On the contrary. Everything points to the fact that the green age represents a new and better quality of life. When the human race's powers of innovation are released, we will drive even smarter cars, live in even better houses – and bask in light and heat from clean sources of energy.

Try to think 20 years ahead to the year 2030.
It is quite impossible for us to have a realistic idea of what the world will look like by then. We will, however, most likely be able to tell our grandchildren weird tales of how we once drove cars that produced noise and smoke, and that we sat around comfortably in garden furniture made out of wood from the rainforests which maintain the CO_2 balance in the atmosphere.

1/20
—
BROTHERS ON BIKES

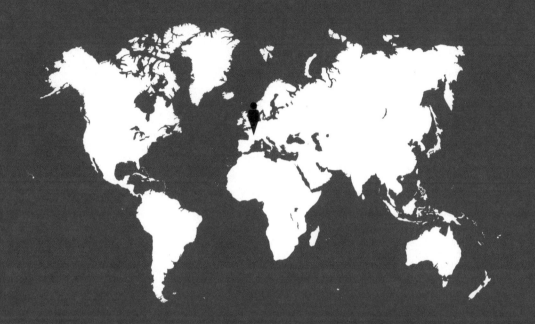

For the tall, slim 40-year-old Jean-Charles Decaux a typical Sunday morning consists of 60 kilometers on bike, dressed in black bike shorts and a black T-shirt. And in the afternoon there will be a pleasant bike ride in the woods with his four-year-old son, who has just learnt the art of riding a bike. Perhaps that is one of the reasons why Jean-Charles Decaux took the opportunity to reinvent the bike as a means of transport in Paris, the French megapolis. The French company JCDecaux, where he is the managing director, is owned by the Decaux family, and it actually makes its money in outdoor advertising. In any case the French businessman was right. In co-operation with his ten year older brother Jean-Francois, he has not only reintroduced city bikes in Paris, he has also exported them to more than

100 million users in 60 major cities in France and abroad.

Ten years ago Jean-Charles Decaux and his company for the first time felt green vibrations from the customers, the partners and the municipalities with which they co-operated: "We quickly realized that the bike could be a major breakthrough for our company, as well as for the urban environment, the municipalities, and for transport companies all over the world. However, our approach to the project was not the bike as such. It was the service which the bike could render our target group. We have revolutionized the use of the product, not the product itself."

Jean-Charles Decaux is wearing a dark blue, pinstriped suit and when a sunbeam slides through the large windows in the sofa corner in his office, the slim gold ring on the ring finger on his left hand glimmers. Jean-Charles and his brother are in charge of the company, which their father founded in 1964 on the basis of a single contract to build bus shelters in Lyon. Today, the company is the world's second largest of its kind and it focuses on outdoor advertising, street furniture, billboard advertising and advertisements in the transport industry.

The Decaux brothers did not get the idea for the city bike, nor were they the first to put the idea into operation. However, they have managed to turn it into a sustainable business in more than one sense. The success in Paris and in other cities surpasses all other attempts to introduce bikes into the urban environment. Five years ago, one would be lucky to get a glimpse of a bike in the busy streets of Paris. In France and in most of southern Europe, the bike is not generally used as a means of transportation, and to many Parisians a ped-

CITYBIKES

—

Paris supplies the tarmac to the world's largest city bike solution. More than 20.600 silver-grey city bikes and 1450 bike stations have been strategically integrated into the city's public transport system. Every year, this type of green transport saves the city 25,000 tons of CO_2 emission, as well as a considerable amount of traffic jams.

In July 2007, the city bike was introduced in Paris. The social democratic mayor Bertrand Delanoë took the initiative and his partner was the world's second largest outdoor advertising company. The company paid the expenses in return for advertising space in the city.

The city bike solution has been exported to 60 other cities in France and abroad – among others Lyon, Nantes, Toulouse, Marseille, Seville, Luxembourg, Brussels, and soon it will also be implemented in London, Dublin and Brisbane. Today, the city bikes have more than 100 million users worldwide.

—

> ""
> # WITHOUT A SUSTAINABLE BUSINESS MODEL THERE CAN BE NO GREEN INNOVATION.
> ""

al bike is little more than a distant childhood memory. Biking is a sport for the few – such as the heroes in Tour de France. However, today 20.600 silver-gray, silent city bikes are in use in the streets of Paris. The so-called Vélib', whose name is a compilation of "vélo" and "liberté" – bike and freedom – became a part of the urban landscape on 15 July 2007. Already a few months after their introduction, thousands of Frenchmen were forced to use them. The metro personnel, the bus- and train drivers went on strike and the main thoroughfares of the city were paralyzed, while the Vélib' was untouched by the strike.

Today the city of Paris is full of bike parking sites, to the extent that there is always a bike in your vicinity. JCDecaux protects itself against theft by letting the users pay with credit cards, so they can be located again. The city bikes are a part of the urban public transport system and they can be found next to metro and railway stations, and near bus stops. Here they are parked on average 10-15 times every day. The green extension of the traditional transport system is available around the clock. The first thirty minutes are free if you buy a subscription – one Euro a day, five Euros

JEAN-CHARLES DECAUX (1969)
—

Managing director of JCDecaux. He began working for the company at the age of 21 and two years later in 1991 he was promoted to CEO in a subsidiary in Spain. In 1994, he added Asia and Latin America to his portfolio, and since the year 2000 he has managed the company with his ten year older brother Jean-Francois Decaux. JCDecaux is now the world's second largest company focusing on outdoor advertising, street furniture, billboard advertising and advertisements in the transport industry. The company was founded in 1964 by their father Jean-Claude Decaux, who invented the concept of street furniture.

In addition to city bikes, JCDecaux offers and maintains free "street furniture" such as shelters near bus stops and public restrooms, etc. in return for the permission to build advertisements into the equipment and thereby gaining a profit. The company employs 9250 people, and is represented in 55 countries and 3400 cities. In 2008 its turnover amounted to 2168 million Euros.
—

a week and 29 Euros for a whole year. You can park the bike in any Vélib' parking. The distance between each is a maximum of 300 meters. For this reason it is often quicker to get around by Vélib than by car, bus or metro.

The Decaux brothers' concept is not only an incredibly successful business. It is also a solution and an efficient weapon in the battle against city traffic. More than 100 million users in 60 cities can testify to this. So far, the battle against traffic in the major cities has offered only a few rays of hope - for instance the experiments with turnpike money in London and in Stockholm. 80% of global CO_2 emissions originate from the major cities of the world. Road transport is the major culprit – and the rest of the factors are increasing steadily all over the world. Among climate experts it is a well known fact that passenger cars and trucks constitute one of the greatest

challenges, since it will still be a while before we have feasible alternatives to petrol or diesel driven cars.

Every time you press down a pedal, the city is spared sound pollution as well as CO_2 emission. During the first year after the introduction of the Vélib', the car traffic in Paris dropped by 5% and every year the urban bike saves the city 25,000 tons of CO_2. The city bikes are mended, oiled and repaired by maintenance personnel that regularly visit the bike stations in their gas driven vehicles and on electric bikes, or they ship the Vélib's to a workshop on a barge on the Seine. The Vélib's are cleaned with rainwater caught on the roofs of the JCDecaux locations. The anti-graffiti product is ecological and the bikes are 99% recyclable.

The world's second largest outdoor advertising company has not filled the city

with bikes in order to spare the environment and save the world. The green wave touches everyone – consumers, politicians, and the business community – and there is money to be made on green solutions. Such projects are in need of business models that produce a profitable bottom line: "If it should make sense to involve a company like ours, which has 10,000 employees, in a green project such as this one, then we will have to have an economically feasible business model. Otherwise there will be no profit. That is the way it is, whether you like it or not. No business model equals no green projects in the world. It is not popular to say this, but I am not a politician. I am an entrepreneur and a businessman," says Jean-Charles Decaux.

With regard to the Vélib', JCDecaux has found an appropriate business model. The rented bike solution is financed by the company, which paid the seed money of around 90 million Euros and employs around 285 people to run the system and repair the bikes. In return, JCDecaux has the sole and exclusive rights to 1628 of the city's billboards. The city has exchanged the rights to advertising on billboards for the bike solution. The brothers' experiment proves that green initiatives can actually unfold, when the business community makes sure that they are founded on economically feasible business models: "The green spirit and the business community should not be afraid of each other. We must work together. Green initiatives are often perceived as the enemies of the business world. But that is a misconception. Only the business world can improve our community. It is necessary to have the business community and the companies onboard. If they co-operate they can make much bigger changes than the gov-

THE DRIVING FORCE BEHIND GREEN INNOVATION ACCORDING TO JEAN-CHARLES DECAUX

—

■ "Curiosity and production are the two most important factors. In attempts to understand why or why not, one should constantly reconsider and wonder. As an adult one has to force oneself to have the curiosity of a child."

■ "The next step is to put your idea into production. There are lots of ideas in the world, so it is important to realize your ideas, find a market, and create a business model. Otherwise it is just another idea."

—

ernments worldwide. If the world's 1000 largest companies found green business models we would be able to change the world much faster than via the G20. Much faster indeed. Whether you like it or not, the world is run by the companies."

The city bike concept has found its way to 60 cities – Lyon, Toulouse, Brussels and Luxembourg, and it is coming to London, Dublin and Brisbane. Many cities are looking for a solution to the chaotic traffic and intense exhaust problems of the rush hours and are considering the possibility of implementing green and fast city transport. At JCDecaux, the future is focused on conquering new markets, new cities: "So before we move into other business areas or invent new green concepts, we want to explore the Véleb´ concept. There is a large market, if we do it well – and only if we do it right."

THE FIFTH
INDUSTRIAL
REVOLUTION

It is in all probability evident to the reader that the keynote of this book is not minor. There is a reason for that, over and above the fact that a book about innovation almost automatically will demonstrate a firm belief in technological landslides, and in the brilliant brains and ideas of certain nerds. The reason is that even if we in this day and age are facing an uncanny challenge, this time we will be able to make an effort and create a master plan to solve the problem via a comprehensive, worldwide vision and strategy.

The global, digital revolution of the 1990s happened organically, more or less of its own accord. Of course industrial policies were planned across the globe and there was a desire to create new growth and new attractive high tech jobs. However, there was no general decision that we should have an Internet, a Facebook, and a global electronic mail system. That just happened. In terms of the green in-

> "
> FIRST, I BELIEVE THAT THIS NATION SHOULD COMMIT ITSELF TO ACHIEVING THE GOAL, BEFORE THIS DECADE IS OUT, OF LANDING A MAN ON THE MOON AND RETURNING HIM SAFELY TO THE EARTH. NO SINGLE SPACE PROJECT IN THIS PERIOD WILL BE MORE IMPRESSIVE TO MANKIND, OR MORE IMPORTANT FOR THE LONG-RANGE EXPLORATION OF SPACE; AND NONE WILL BE SO DIFFICULT OR EXPENSIVE TO ACCOMPLISH... BUT IN A VERY REAL SENSE, IT WILL NOT BE ONE MAN GOING TO THE MOON-IF WE MAKE THIS JUDGMENT AFFIRMATIVELY, IT WILL BE AN ENTIRE NATION. FOR ALL OF US MUST WORK TO PUT HIM THERE.
> "
>
> **John F. Kennedy,**
> American præsident, 1961

novation boom, the opposite scenario applies. Possibly for the first time in world history, decision makers from every country on the globe have committed themselves to the fact that we *must* undertake a technological quantum leap. We *have to* embrace solar panels, hydrogen trains, and geothermal power. We have got to use bioenergy to run planes, efficient district heating systems, and zero energy houses. Furthermore, we must make use of all available means.

The master plan is in the making. Since 2005-2006 a growing number of governments around the globe have realized that global warming is a problem which must be solved, and that it can only happen in a global joint venture. One by one they have committed themselves to co-operate under the auspices of the UN, our global institution designed for purposes such as this. On the basis of the international laws, introduced by the UN in Rio in 1992 and passed in Kyoto in 1997, the UN officials have continued the negotiations about an agreement which will unite all countries in a legally binding co-operation to combat climate change. In 2007 on the holiday island of Bali in Indonesia, 192 countries agreed to prepare a convention, which through political, economic, and legal instruments orchestrate a worldwide teamwork on a scale never seen before. In short, a master plan to solve the climate problem.

In the acronym loving UN, the negotiation meetings are called COP, signifying Conference of Parties, i.e. meetings between the parties behind the convention. The first COP was held in Berlin in 1995. The fifteenth, COP15 was held in Copenhagen in 2009 with the express purpose of agreeing the master plan.

The historical parallel, which many people tend to draw in terms of this innovative task facing the global community, is the American mission of the 1960s to put a man on the moon – and back to Earth in one piece. Even if there are great differences – not least because of the necessity dictated by the climate crisis – one can make pedagogical comparisons. When rereading Kennedy's "Special Message to the Congress on Urgent National Needs" from 25 May 1961, it not only encompasses an historical vision of getting to the moon within a decade, but also a catalogue of the initiatives necessary to realize the vision. Kennedy asked for exorbitant amounts of money to develop new rocket motors, satellites, and a weather prognosis system. He named all the leading figures in The National Space Council, and he made it clear that all research resources would be earmarked for the moon landing. Finally, he made it clear, that nobody knew

if the adventure would succeed, and what it would entail.

In many ways we are on the verge of embarking on a similar project here on the threshold of the 2010s. However, this time we are talking about a journey that will save mankind. It will be an organized global effort which will encompass everything from enormous co-ordinated investments into research, development and demonstration projects, barrier-breaking technological collaboration, and shared global standards with regard to capping global emissions, financial support from the rich to the poor, and economic sanctions against those who do not abide by the rules of the convention. In other words, agreements about global joint ventures, which would have appeared avant-garde to any citizen of the world who lived in Kennedy's day and age.

In this perspective – and in spite of the threats of doomsday – it is difficult to remain a confirmed pessimist. Think of what we have previously accomplished without a global teamwork. This time we have every right to expect results on a scale never seen before, as a result of an historical, global exertion, which ultimately only serves one purpose: to drive radical low carbon innovation. "A vision without a plan is an illusion," says the charismatic and eloquent James E. Rogers, CEO of Duke Energy, the third largest energy company in the USA. Rogers is a veteran in American climate and energy politics, and he often chastises politicians, not least those from the USA, for talking about how to prevent global warming and reduce the emissions by 2050, but not about how they plan to do it. This time we are actually in a different situation. We can have a vision as well as a plan.

The climate crisis places us in a unique historical situation. For the first time in the history of the world, we know the threats, before they will begin to take effect, and we have the opportunity to plan an industrial revolution. If we go back in history 250 years, we can identify four industrial revolutions. They vary in extent, geographical range and context, but they have a number of shared characteristics. They were influenced by certain technologies and forms of transport and communication – from the steam engine, the assembly line, the passenger plane to the Internet. Their common traits were that they created inconceivable economic growth in some parts of the globe, and that they created an imbalance in the global ecosystems.

On the basis of decades of scientific co-operation on a global level, among other places in UN contexts, we know the natural consequences of imbalance and we are able to construct models that predict scenarios of the distant future. During the past twenty years the research teamwork in the IPPC, the Intergovernmental Panel on Climate Change, established in 1989 by the UN Environmental Program and the World Meteorological Organization, has created a unique level of knowledge unparalleled in history. In a similar vein science and the experts have developed an advanced catalogue of ideas describing potential solutions to the problem. These initiatives enable us to design the revolution. We can ensure that it will be global and total, and that it rectifies the ecological imbalance created by the four previous revolutions. That is the challenge we must embrace and by implementing a master plan, we can ensure that it happens in responsible ways.

AND
THEN
THERE
WAS
LIGHT

1.

2.

1.
This is what the World looked like photo-graphed from one of NASA's satellites on a night in 2007. The sea of lights clearly shows how human activity influences the planet.

2.
... And this is what the world in all likeli-hood will look like in 2030 according to the best available data. The enormous growth, particularly in countries like China and India, constitutes a gigantic challenge. There is nothing wrong with the fact that most of the globe is covered in light. Our mutual challenge consists in the fact that the light must originate from new, renewa-ble sources of energy.

2/20
—
THE EMPEROR OF THE SUN

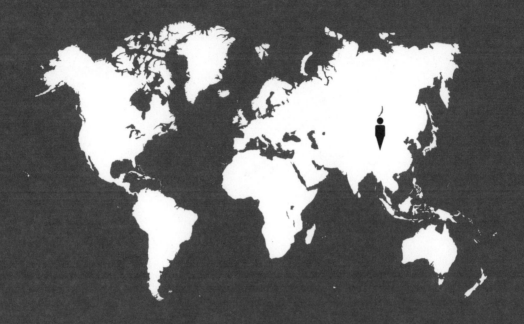

From waiter to Sun King. That could be the heading of Dr. Zhengrong Shi's life so far. Twenty years ago, Shi worked as a waiter to be able to afford his PhD studies at the University of New South Wales. Today, the 46-year-old Shi goes by the name of "the Sun King". Nobody could be more surprised at his success and instant career than Shi himself. "I never thought this solar business could take off or become commercially viable. I thought I just needed to concentrate on my research and publish papers to do my job as a scientist," says Shi.

Shi still thinks of himself as a scientist first and foremost. He's one of the world's most respected experts on solar technologies, in particular thin-film modules. He holds nearly a dozen patents in the field of photovoltaic (PV) technologies. However, according to *Forbes*

DR. ZHENGRONG SHI (1966)
—
Is Suntechs founder, chairman, and CEO. Prior to setting up Suntech in 2001, he was a research director and executive director of Pacific Solar Pty., Ltd., an Australian photovoltaic (PV) company engaged in the commercialization of next-generation thin-film technology. Dr. Shi holds 11 patents in PV technologies. He received a bachelor's degree in optical science from Jilin University in China in 1983, a master's degree in laser physics from the Shanghai Institute of Optics and Fine Mechanics, the Chinese Academy of Sciences, in 1986, and a PhD in electrical engineering from the University of New South Wales, Australia, in 1992.
—

magazine, he is also the richest man in China, with a net worth of $3 billion. Furthermore, he is the chairman and CEO of Suntech Power Holdings Co. Ltd., a company he founded in 2001.

The Suntech company began as a modest venture. In 2001, the authorities in the Chinese suburb of Wuxi on the western edge of Shanghai, lured Shi with $6 million to finance a solar company. Four years later, by which time Shi had acquired the shares of his sponsors, Suntech went public on the New York Stock Exchange. Solar technology took off, and overnight Suntech was worth $5.5 billion and Shi was a billionaire. By January 2009, Suntech was the world's largest solar panel manufacturer.

From the beginning, Shi has relentlessly pursued the solutions to two problems: he wanted to improve the efficiency of solar panels – the percentage of sunlight converted to electricity – and to reduce the cost per unit as quickly as possible. The company is committed to solving these two problems. Innovation is a core business strategy for the company, and Shi says it will remain so. Suntech has set multiple conversion efficiency records with its PV panels.

Working for 15 years as a research scientist before becoming a businessman helped convince Shi that there was no shortage of energy on the globe. What was missing was clean electricity accessible to the people.

To meet the demand, Suntech was the first company to set up a megawatt-scale production facility in China. In each of the past five years, says Shi, Suntech has increased capacity by 20% or more. Early in 2009, the company marked a global first: its assembly lines were capable of producing one gigawatt (GW) of solar panels in one year, or 1,000 megawatts (MW), equivalent to one large coal-fired power plant.

Suntech's breakneck growth might lead one to believe that Shi merely had to match a good product with pent-up demand. Not so. As is the case with any emerging industry rushing toward maturity, winning over skeptical government officials and fickle consumers

BETTER AND CHEAPER SOLAR CELLS

—

Suntech's nearly 250-strong research and development team based in Wuxi, China, works to improve the efficiency and reduce the cost of an assortment of solar technologies. In the first phase of commercialization is the company's Pluto technology, which applies monocrystalline photovoltaic (PV) cells and polycrystalline PV cells.

"Monocrystalline" panels have a smooth, unbroken appearance and are made using cells cut from a single cylindrical crystal of silicon; they are generally the most efficient type of PV panel. "Polycrystalline" panels have a fractured, broken appearance and are made from cells cut from a block of melted and re-crystallized silicon; they are generally cheaper to manufacture, but less efficient than monocrystalline PV panels. Suntech is working to develop new and improved materials – among others upgraded metallurgical silicon, EVA, glass, and modular backsheets – in order to make the solar energy products better and cheaper. Suntech is also leading in the field of thin-film solar technology.

—

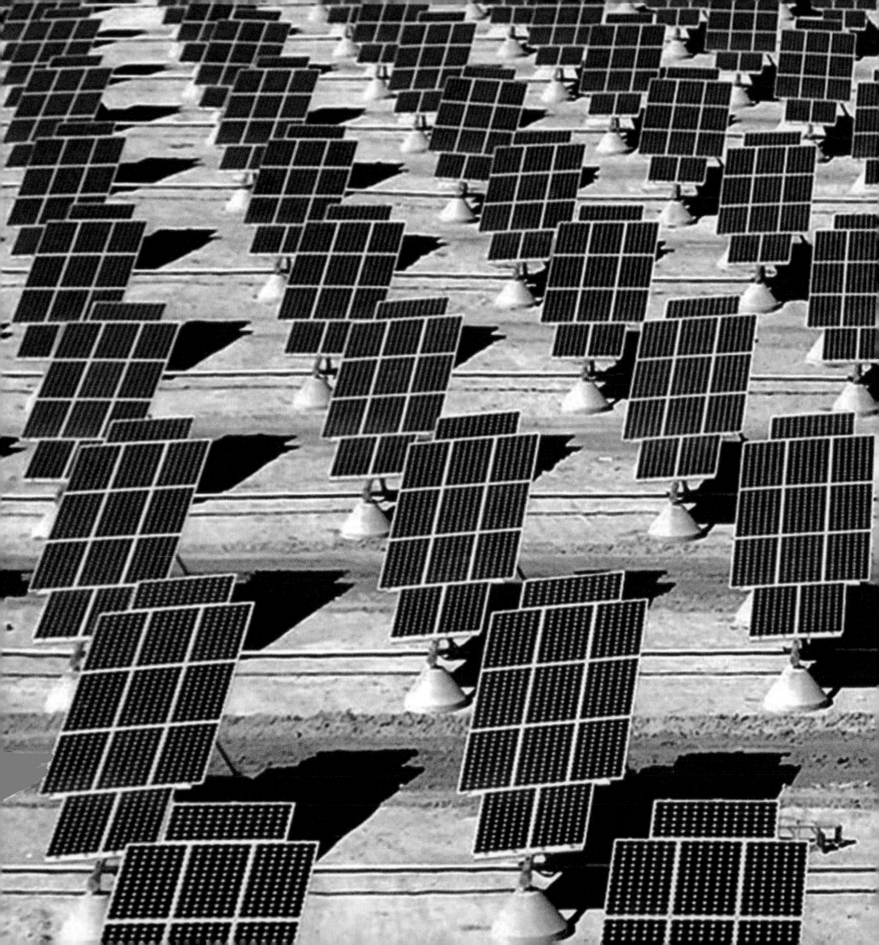

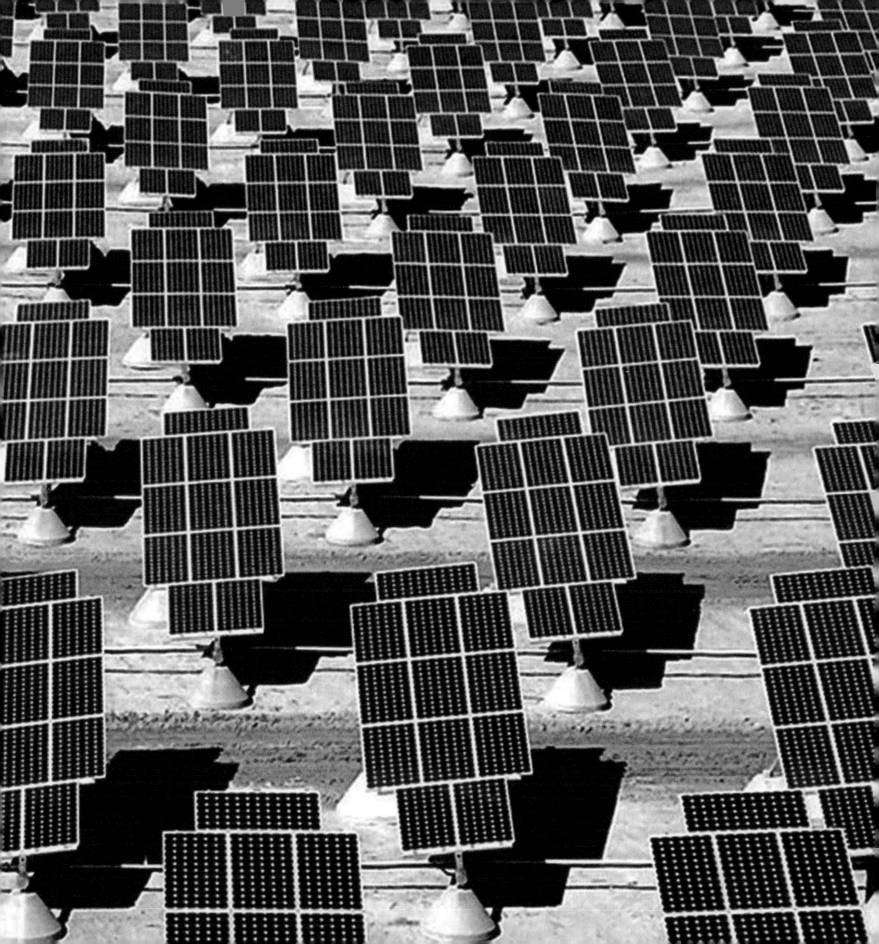

> **"**
> ## MY BELIEF, MY PHILOSOPHY IS AS FOLLOWS: HUMAN BEINGS HAVE TO BE BRAVE ENOUGH TO TRY EVERYTHING. IF YOU NEVER TRY, IT WILL NEVER HAPPEN.
> **"**

proved - and remains - difficult. "Solar energy is a new industry," says Shi and continues: "Four or five years ago, solar was a parasitic industry. It had to rely on materials from other industries" – such as silicon companies that produce elements for computerchips. Now the whole industry is much more advanced."

Despite the seed money from the city of Wuxi, Suntech has had to fight to sell its idea to government officials with "a lot of doubts about costs and scalability." Architects, building engineers, and regulators have had to be convinced that Building Integrated Photovoltaics (BIPV) are not too expensive, that they can be used as building material, and that they conform to building codes.

And, yes, the sticky issue of cost. Photovoltaics still cost about $0.25-0.30 per kilowatt-hour (kWh). Although that's already competitive during peak hours in places with high electricity rates such as California, it's still much higher than the average price of electricity in the U.S: $0.10-0.12/kWh.However, in sunny areas like California solar panels now deliver electricity at competitive prices.

Nevertheless, Shi is confident that the cost barrier will come down. He expects grid parity – that is, for his products to compete on a cost basis with electricity from fossil-fuel sources as well as other renewable energy sources such as wind – in three to four years. In some regions, parity will come sooner, others longer, but Shi has no doubt that costs will come down.

"This is in line with what people want," says Shi, a reduction in cost, and a better product. But, he is very quick to add, "It is up to *us* to make it work - not the government."

The foundation and growth of Suntech have overlapped with a growing global awareness of the threat posed by climate change. Shi has taken that threat as a call to action. "We have changed our family life to be very green," he says. But Shi's commitment goes much deeper. Over the past three or four years, he has become increasingly outspoken. He wants to raise awareness and advocate for policy changes. He gives speeches throughout China, he talks to government officials. It's all part of his desire to make people more aware of climate change, to encourage them to change their lifestyle, and to "multiply his *personal* awareness."

Within Suntech, Shi's climate change awareness has been adopted as the way to do business. It's an effort, says Shi, to lead by example. "We want to encourage all employees

THE DRIVING FORCE BEHIND GREEN INNOVATION ACCORDING TO DR. ZHENGRONG SHI

—

■ **Our product solves some of the problems created by climate change. However, it must also make a profit.**
■ **Leading by example. "We want to encourage all employees in the company to have a green lifestyle," says Shi.**

—

in our company to have a green lifestyle." At company facilities, day-lighting is encouraged to avoid the need for artificial light, thermostats are set to save energy in winter and summer, bottled water isn't allowed, and lights are turned off, when the last person leaves for the day. "They're small things," admits Shi, "but they add up to make a difference."

Asked about his hope for the future, Shi doesn't hesitate with his reply: "I'm quite optimistic about the future. There are a lot of problems. But more people, more governments, are becoming aware of the problems. If we can involve politicians, we can secure our future. My belief, my philosophy is as follows: Human beings have to be brave enough to try everything. If you never try, it will never happen."

LIGHT DAWNS

—

Normally we perceive energy as a resource which is hard to gain access to, which must be mined or pumped up from the ground. However, every day of the year non-polluting clean energy comes our way – free of charge. The rays of the sun are extremely forceful. In a span of forty minutes the sun beams enough electrons to the earth to cover the energy consumption of the entire globe for a year. The problem is that so far we have only done very limited research into how we can capture and apply this energy. So far we have spent 100 years developing advanced car motors and 50 years building satellites. In comparison the solar industry is only a few decades old. The technology is rudimentary and the investments in solar energy have been extremely limited. Until now.

The potential in the technology that we already have is great. According to the magazine *Scientific American* it is possible to cover 69 percent of the energy consumption in the USA and 35 percent of the energy consumption in 2050 by building solar farms in the sunny south western part of the USA in an area twice the size of Denmark. A network of solar energy farms the size of Wales and located in the Sahara would be able to supply all of Europe with all the electricity it needs. A number of energy experts suggest that a joint African European solar energy project should be developed and their idea is supported by among others the EU's energy research center. According to the plans, the energy should be transported to Europe through advanced fiber-optic cables.

Illustration
An abundant resource
—
There is plenty of solar energy available in the USA - if we capture and apply it. The white circles show the size of the solar farms needed to cover 69 percent of America's electricity consumption by the year 2050.

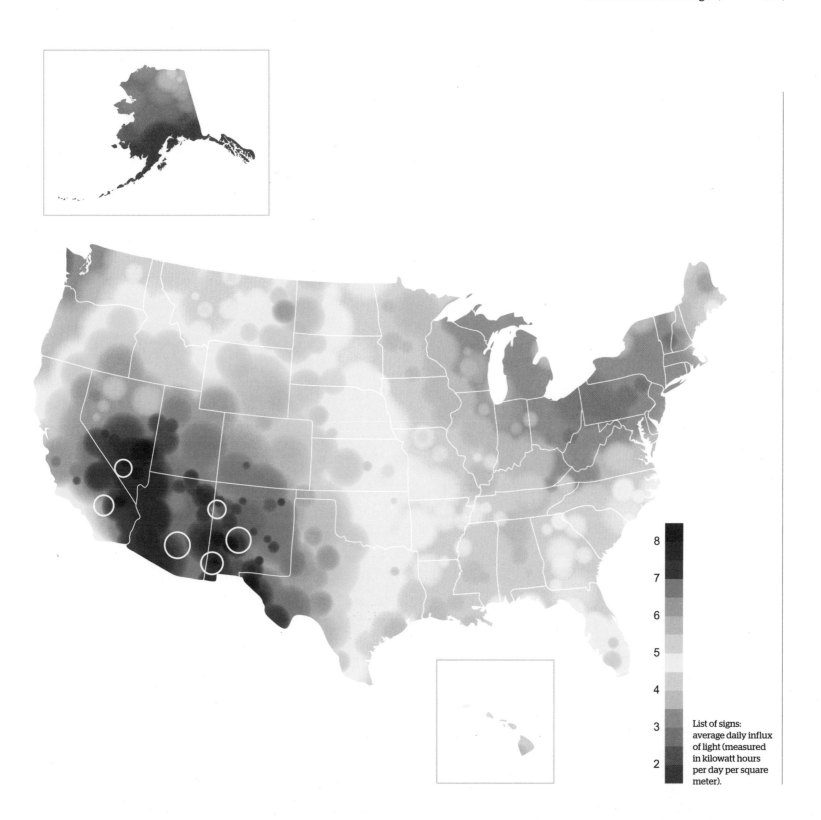

List of signs: average daily influx of light (measured in kilowatt hours per day per square meter).

3/20
—
EVERYTHING ON EARTH HAS **VALUE**

One of the main achievements of the global environmental movement was that ordinary citizens during the 1970s and 1980s became aware of the fact that the planet's forests are "the lungs of the world" and in this capacity an essential factor in the cycle of the planet. This did not prevent deforestation, but it created the basis for a strong democratic support of the politicians who are trying to protect the large forests. Today, the metaphor has a new and even more important significance. The trees not only "exhale" oxygen, they also "inhale" CO_2 and now we know that they keep unfathomable amounts of CO_2 greenhouse gasses out of the atmosphere. Every second the forests render the planet an invaluable "CO_2 service".

Uganda in East Africa spans vast areas of tropical rainforest, but they are disappearing

ABASI MUSISI (1951)

—

Born in Kampala, the capital of Uganda. He owns and runs the coffee roasting plant Nguvu, which he founded in 1980. Besides the coffee roasting plant, he owns the company Kampala Jellitone Suppliers Ltd, which produces briquettes made of waste from the farming sector. Abasi Musisi has also invented a special stove purpose-built for the green briquettes.

—

at an alarming rate, partly because the wood is used as firewood and for the production of charcoal, partly because the space is needed for urban expansion. In 1990, there were 5 million hectares of forest in Uganda. Today, the deforestation has taken its toll to the extent that only 3.5 million hectares are left. In 40 years, there will be no more forests left in the African nation, if this development continues. For this reason a journey through the green fertile landscapes of Uganda is a thought-provoking experience. Particularly in the area around the capital of Kampala, there are large areas characterized by tree stumps and scorched earth. In Kampala, the city's green breathing spaces are disappearing, and instead shopping centers and apartment houses are built in their place. For most Ugandans a roof over their heads or a little shop that can bring in a secure income is more important than the rainforest and the climate of the planet. The same scenario applies to other places on the African continent and in other countries with large, tropical forests such as Indonesia and South America.

Today, deforestation is responsible for around 30% of the global CO_2-problem. In other words, we can solve 30% of the problem if we conserve the remaining forests. So if anyone lives up to the cliché of "making a difference", it is Abasi Musisi. His invention is already putting a damper on the deforestation in Uganda, and in the future it will help make a difference at a global level. We are heading for his factory on a dirt road full of potholes on the outskirts of Kampala. Abasi Musisi has invented a new type of briquette made of waste which can replace traditional fuel. His technology has transformed waste to fuel and can replace the expensive, smelly, and polluting charcoal, which is used in 90% of Ugandan households. Abasi Musisi's invention saves more than 6

tons of CO_2 for each ton of briquettes. Since the factory produces more than 1500 tons of briquettes a year, this equals an emission reduction of more than 9000 tons of CO_2 every year. In the lifetime of the factory, the briquettes have replaced 6900 tons of wood, which equals more than 35,000 tons of CO_2.

Musisi's green invention is a simple solution to a complex problem. What began as a thought in the mind of a man living in a suburb of Kampala has now become a recognized solution, and one of the many answers to the world's growing environmental challenges. "It is about providing people with a viable alternative. It is no good telling a poor farmer that he should travel first class, if he doesn't have that option. The same goes for fuel. There

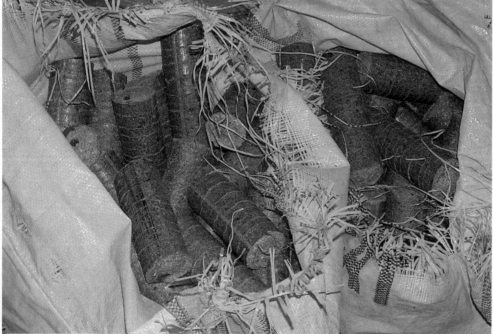

BURNING WASTE

—

Abasi Musisi has invented a briquette made from farming waste. It can replace the use of traditional fuel. The briquettes are cheap, clean and they prevent the deforestation in Uganda. It took around ten years to develop the briquettes.
Kampala Jellitone Suppliers Ltd. has the capacity to produce 2000 briquettes a year
Almost 6000 briquettes have been sold
The briquettes have saved more than 6900 tons of wood.
In all, more than 35,000 tons of CO_2 have been saved.

—

should be a feasible alternative," says Musisi, while we wait at the gate to the factory, where the briquettes are made.

"Welcome to my factory," says Abasi Musisi. He is already inspecting and giving orders before he gets out of the car.

Coming from a humble background, it can be difficult to imagine that a product from Abasi Musisi's factory has made an impact on the international environmental agenda. In the factory yard and in the surrounding small open houses, men and women in blue boiler suits are busy producing the daily output of briquettes. The manager himself is wearing

1. The small, compact briquettes of compressed farming waste do not pollute. Furthermore they are clean and easy to handle in a kitchen.

a newly ironed white shirt and a pair of nice pants. However, the clothes are already full of dust, since he cannot help checking the bags while showing us his life's work.

"Can you see what this is?" he asks in the same way that a teacher tests a pupil. He takes a fistful of peanut shells from a bag, answers the question himself, and scoops up a new handful. "And these are what remains of the corncobs, when the corn has been removed, shells from coffee beans, cocoa beans, rice shells – it is all waste," he says proudly.

The main industry in Uganda is farming. Around 90 % of the population is employed in the farming sector and the waste that is used in the production of the briquettes primarily originates from farms and plantations. Abassi Musisi collects the waste and it does not cost him anything. Most farmers are only too happy to get rid of it, so instead of accumulating along roads or in flammable stacks around houses and huts, it now goes into sacks that are sent to the factory. In the factory, the waste is poured through a sieve, dried, measured and weighed, and then processed by a number of machines imported from Europe and India. Finally, the contents of the large sacks are reduced to a compact briquette.

"It is like baking a cake. The proportions must be completely right. Otherwise the recipe does not yield the desired result," says Musisi. The company, *Kampala Jellitone Suppliers*, produces around 130 tons of briquettes every month. The briquettes leave the factory in an old truck and are transported to various types of companies such as breweries and bakeries, as well as to 30 schools, universities, hospitals and restaurants, which use the briquettes in their large kitchens. The briquettes are compact and efficient and this is a great advantage to the kitchens. The briquettes pollute less, they are much cheaper than charcoal and the cooking is faster. Before the invention of the briquettes, the cook would have to arrive at the school at three a.m. in order to light the stoves. Thanks to the briquettes, he can now sleep till six a.m.

"I am worried about our climate. My brain and my heart tell me that it is important to take action, and that is what I have done. I am proud of the fact that I have created a practical and concrete alternative, and that I am not just someone who preaches from a pulpit. I have started something that will live on, even when I am no longer here," says the man who invented the briquettes.

A few miles from the factory where the briquettes are manufactured, you find the real cause of Abasi Musisi's hunt for alternative fuel: the coffee roasting business *Nguvu*. In 1980, Musisi founded the coffee roasting business at a time when the price of petroleum, gas and other fuels went through the roof. This prompted Musisi to change his way of roasting

THE DRIVING FORCE BEHIND GREEN INNOVATION ACCORDING TO ABASI MUSISI

—

■ **The wish to create something that will still exist, when I am gone.**
■ **A concrete need to find a fuel that can make the day-to-day life in my factory cheaper and more sustainable.**

—

coffee beans. Like Gyro Gearloose he experimented like a madman in an attempt to find the right recipe. He consulted the local university and western engineers, and after more than 10 years and 100 attempts, he succeeded in inventing the briquette. Musisi has now sold almost 6000 tons of the briquette for which he has won international prizes.

"International recognition is important for me, since it is not easy to be a pioneer in Africa," says Abasi Musisi, who has encountered plenty of opposition in his own country. "The government in Uganda did not believe in me. They do not believe in an ordinary man without a title and a long academic education. In the beginning, I was constantly asked if I had a PhD. In this country you have to be somebody in order to become somebody." However, Abasi Musisi remained undeterred, because he has in fact been a pioneer and an innovator since he was a little boy. When he was eight years old and went to the local school, he manufactured small toy cars, repaired pots and pans and made balls of compressed plant fibers in order to impress his school friends. "I always wanted to be a famous inventor. When

I read about the people who had invented the airplane and the radio, I wished I were one of them," Musisi says.

To Abasi Musisi it is not the actual product that determines if he wants to take an interest in it. When he decided to go into the coffee roasting business, it was not because he loves to drink coffee. It was because he saw a chance to create a successful business. Before the coffee adventure he had created a company, that produced beauty products for women, but the raw materials were too expensive to import. However, there was an abundance of coffee beans in Uganda.

"It is all about creating something," says Musisi, who grew up as an orphan without access to great means. His mother died, when he was one year old, and he never saw his father. Instead his grandmother nurtured him and gave him a good upbringing. "My grandmother always told me that I would become a mechanic or an engineer," he says and stresses that his difficult background only made him work harder to reach his goal.

"It took me ten years to develop the briquettes and I have encountered much opposition, not just from the government. Most people just told me to stick to the coffee roasting. Many people thought I was crazy, but the people who invented the airplane, the telephone, and the radio were in the same situation – and today we cannot imagine a world without those things. It is about having a vision and isolating yourself in your room and keep on keeping on," says Abasi Musisi, who spends more time in his own brain than with family and friends. The green innovator does not have time for social activities. The only thing he has time for – besides work – is his religion. Like most Ugandans he is profoundly religious and gives God the credit for his success. "It is a gift from God – I put everything in his hands," says Abasi Musisi who has already mapped out his future dream.

"I have plans of building a large factory that can supply the entire region and the whole of Africa. When even waste can be turned into gold, I know that everything on earth has value. Now that I have come this far, I cannot just stop here. I would like to see the little man from Uganda be mentioned in important international books."

"

MANY PEOPLE THOUGHT I WAS CRAZY, BUT THE PEOPLE WHO INVENTED THE AIRPLANE, THE TELEPHONE, AND THE RADIO WERE IN THE SAME SITUATION – AND TODAY WE CANNOT IMAGINE A WORLD WITHOUT THOSE THINGS...

"

WHEN I LOOK AT THIS IMAGE, TWO THOUGHTS COME INTO MY MIND. THE FIRST IS HOW BEAUTIFUL OUR PLANET IS. AND SECONDLY: **WE HAVE NO OTHER PLACE TO GO.**

Steven Chu,
American Secretary of Energy,
Nobel Laureate in Physics.
—

The Blue Planet Earth, photographed in
1968 from the spacecraft Apollo 8.

WITHOUT
MERCY

—

The climate change are merciless and those who have contributed the least to the problem will suffer the most. The present concentration of greenhouse gasses in the atmosphere is mainly caused by the industrial development in the rich parts of the world. The consequences will be worst for Africa.

According to the UN's climate panel, Africa can among other things expect that the shortage of water will increase, the areas suitable for farming will be reduced, the seasons ideal for cultivation will be shorter, the risk of floods, for instance after heavy rains, will be greater, and there will be an increased frequency of climate related diseases such as e.g. malaria, malnutrition, and diarrhea. The destruction of coral reefs and mangrove forests will also be comprehensive. As a result, the income from tourism and fishing will decrease, and the depletion of the fish stock in the lakes will continue.

Illustration
1. **A historical perspective of CO_2 emissions.**
2. **Climate mortality.**
—
The two world maps illustrate the unfairness of global warming. Map 1 shows the CO_2 emissions throughout history, distributed according to country.
Map 2 shows the extent to which countries are exposed to diseases such as diarrhea, malaria, and malnutrition as a result of global warming.

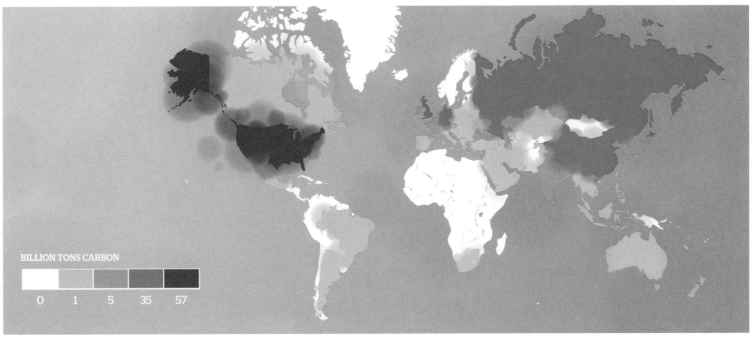

BILLION TONS CARBON

| 0 | 1 | 5 | 35 | 57 |

1.

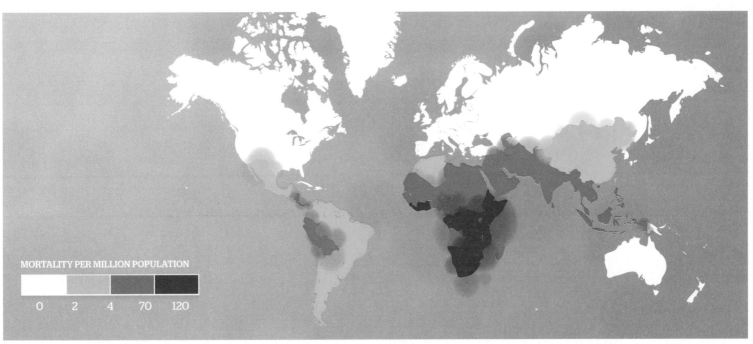

MORTALITY PER MILLION POPULATION

| 0 | 2 | 4 | 70 | 120 |

2.

4/20
—
GOOD ENERGY FOR ALL

It is no coincidence that Juliet Davenport selected the Roots and Shoots project in one of the gloomiest areas in inner city London. Tucked away behind apartment houses, the project is located in a green square with fragrant climbing roses, apple trees, a full greenhouse and a good-sized walnut tree. During WWII a row of military barracks occupied this space. Today the area hosts a nature school, where around 1000 children drop in during every season in order to learn about spiders, plants, bee-keeping and the water supply of London. The buildings are state-of-the-art and on the rooftops we find the very reason why Juliet Davenport wants us to meet here – solar panels. They supply the school with cheap electricity, and the profit from the surplus electricity contributes to the funding

JULIET DAVENPORT (1968)

—

Graduated in 1989 in physics from Oxford University, specializing in climate. She subsequently took an MA in environment and economy. Then she worked as energy adviser to the European Commission in Brussels. In 1998, she returned to the U.K. and founded the company Unit E, which later became Good Energy. In 2002, she became managing director and has since received a number of prizes for her work, most recently the title of CEO of the Year at this year's Plus+ Awards.

—

of the school. Good Energy, Juliet Davenport's energy company, buys the electricity. Since Roots and Shoots mounted the panels, the project has generated so much electricity, that it could supply enough energy to boil 270,000 cups of tea. Good Energy is the first company in the UK that has specialized in buying and supplying 100 percent green and sustainable energy.

When Juliet Davenport arrives on the square in front of the walnut tree, she is somewhat short of breath. She has made the trip from Paddington Station at full speed in London's heavy morning traffic. When she began studying physics at Oxford University, she never imagined that she would end up as managing director of one of the most lauded energy companies in the UK. However, three years into her education she took a course about the climate and the atmosphere and

"
I DO NOT BELIEVE THAT IT HELPS TO FIGHT OTHER PEOPLE AND, INCIDENTALLY, THAT IS ALSO TIME CONSUMING AND TIRESOME.
"

developed an enduring interest in the subject. "I think that the earliest environmental groups were formed, when people saw the first images of Earth from space. For the first time, the planet was conceived as a fragile place in the vast universe. I had my aha-experience when I saw how sensitive the atmosphere and the climate systems are," she says.

Having completed her physics degree, Juliet Davenport's interest prompted her to study energy and economics. She applied her knowledge working for the European Commission in Brussels, where she advised on energy policies and developed a thorough understanding of Europe's energy supply. During the same period she saw how large sectors of Europe had begun to experiment with renewable energy. However, in Great Britain there was hardly any development at all: "We have some of the greatest natural resources in the region, but of all the European countries we were among the least focused on harnessing those resources and that was a source of immense frustration to me." A random meeting in a hotel in Athens gave Juliet Davenport the idea to transform frustration into business. Having given a speach at a conference on renewable energy, she participated in the reception that followed. "I was standing in one

group of people, talking away. The man, who was to become my future investor, was in the other group, voicing his views. Suddenly we both turned towards each other and initiated a new third conversation," Juliet Davenport remembers.

The subject of the conversation was the fact that governments often focus on economy and sustainability, and forget the social and the human aspects. "Governments like having grand solutions to huge problems. They like to fix it all in one go. Our philosophy was that it is all about involving a large number of people in the actual process and not turning renewable energy into something exclusive. It must be accessible to everyone," she says. Her conversation partner and a German entrepreneur agreed. "Something clicked that night. Two souls found each other." So much so that he –six months after their first meeting – had invested two million pounds in Juliet Davenport's concept of creating an energy company, which sells energy from renewable sources only.

In 1999 when the company started up, it had just four suppliers of renewable energy in the U.K. - including a farmer who sold his milk quote in order to purchase wind turbines, and a couple of old ladies who ran a tea room in the tourist area the Cotswolds with

energy from a water turbine in a half-timbered house in their back garden. "I drove around the country for quite a while in order to find suppliers," Juliet Davenport recalls. On second thoughts, she did not encounter particularly outspoken resistance in the beginning. But she has her own explanation of this situation. "We were so small. When you are small, you are no threat to anyone. I guess people just found me weird," she laughs.

Today very few people would find Juliet Davenport weird. Good Energy has taken the British energy market in its stride. Today the company has a little more than 1000 suppliers and 25,000 customers and Juliet Davenport has just received the CEO of the Year Prize. However, it has been an uphill struggle to change the British population's attitude towards renewable energy. Juliet Davenport

GOOD ENERGY

—

Is the only company in Great Britain that supplies 100 percent renewable energy to its customers. At the outset in 1999, the company only had four suppliers, however, today it has wind turbine parks, and 1000 suppliers who deliver water, wind, and solar energy to the company's 25,000 customers. That means that every year Good Energy prevents the emission of more than 40,000 tons of CO_2. 90 percent of the company's 1700 shareholders are customers. The future goal is to increase the customer base with a factor of ten and to build ten times as many plants that can produce sustainable energy. Today, little more than two percent of U.K.'s energy consumption is supplied by green energy.

—

1. It was party time in August 2007, when bright lights and colors flooded the inauguration of Great Britain's first windturbines park, Delabole in the northern part of Cornwall.

1.

explains: "People quite simply did not believe that we could abandon the use of oil, gas, and fossil fuels. It was not cynicism. It had more to do with the fact that for generations we have been raised to believe that fossil fuels are the only option. That has become an integral part of our mentality."

Today, energy politics are a permanent fixture in the policy of the British government. The awareness of the environmental impact of having large amounts of CO_2 in the atmosphere has increased, but that does not mean that Juliet Davenport feels that she has accomplished her mission. "Sometimes I ask myself if we have accomplished what we set out to do and if it is time to move on. However, much remains to be done here in the U.K., where the percentage of renewable energy is too low,"

says Juliet Davenport. Only two percent of the U.K.'s energy is renewable and our CO_2 emission is increasing.

In the coming years, Good Energy will focus on assisting in the construction of more renewable energy plants. "Right now our greatest problem is the Planning Act. We have a system, where we have enough sustainable energy in the planning process to ensure that we reach our goal, but still the projects tend to get stuck in the system. As a result, our present task is to pave the road for the construction of more renewable energy plants." According to Juliet Davenport, the way to do it is tantalizingly simple. We should place the people and the local communities in the centre. Just to give an example, Good Energy owns a wind farm in Cornwall, where it has held successful

meetings, informing 3000 participants from the local community about the advantages of the project. "A major reason why we got permission to build was that we engaged people and talked to them. I do not believe that it helps to fight other people and, incidentally, that is also time consuming and tiresome. Many entrepreneurs do not feel like talking to people, when they build something unpopular. However, we decided to be different. We brought experts along to the meetings in order to give people proper answers to their questions." Good Energy can pass on that experience, Juliet Davenport says. "We would like to give good advice on how to arrange Open Days. Such an arrangement should involve ordinary people, who have been through the process themselves. Their credibility will convey the fact that it is indeed possible to begin to supply energy. The last thing you should do is to bring in experts, who do not know how to talk to ordinary people. That will be our next challenge."

WIND OF PLENTY

—

At present, wind power covers only a minimal sector of the world's energy consumption. There is, however, plenty of wind to go round. The challenge is to "harvest" the wind where it blows. In 2005 experts from Stanford University were the first to map the global wind power potential, based on available technology and including off shore windturbines stationed along the coastlines. Research shows that in a global perspective there will be 72 terawatts available, which equals the world's energy consumption in the year 2000 times 40. The greatest potential is found along the North American and Northern European coastlines.

Source: Stanford University, 2005

WELCOME TO CLIMATEVILLE

In the course of the next 2-3 decades the cities of the world will change radically due to climate global warming. New and better cities and neighborhoods will flourish, changing our present conceptions of what a city is or should be – from buildings to traffic to city planning and appearance. A major part of the world's CO_2 emission can be traced to the cities, solely because this is where most people live and work. With regard to the figures there is, however, no consensus. Some say that up to 80 percent of the world's cumulative CO_2 emissions originate in the cities, others believe the figure is closer to 40 percent. In any event, the cities will be the centre of a number of initiatives purporting to reduce our CO_2, and in many locations the work has already begun.

City dwellers are by and large much more climate friendly than they are aware of. A city person's CO_2 emission accounts for much less than that of a person who lives in the country, simply because cities consume energy in more efficient ways and offer public transportation. A New Yorker emits only one third of the CO_2 which an average American produces. In London and in Barcelona the inhabitants emit half as much CO_2 as the national average.

In Climateville we will see comprehensive renovations of the existing building

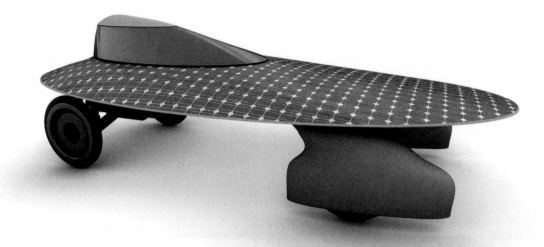

structures – offices, houses, and apartments – because it will be possible to reduce the energy consumption to a minimum with insulation, new windows, and better installations. These investments will to a great extent pay off in the long run. It is not enough to think in terms of new buildings, which make up just a small proportion of the cumulative number of buildings. However, in new structures and neighborhoods we will see houses that are not only energy neutral, but which actually produce energy by using the heat from domestic appliances, electronic installations, and even the inhabitants.

Carbon neutral cities and buildings will mushroom – the first already exist or are in the planning stages in among other places Abu Dhabi, China, USA, and Denmark. In the future we will live closer to each other, because that will generate higher energy efficiency. Highrise blocks are among the most climate friendly constructions on the planet. Our houses will in a very real sense become green. Trees, grass, and plants will proliferate on the roofs of the city, on balconies, and in the cityscapes,

since they both insulate and absorb CO_2.

The distances you will commute to work will be shorter. The work places and the housing will be located in the same neighborhoods. In previous times the city planners placed the factories and the offices in the industrial areas or outside the cities because of the noise and the pollution. However, as far as most work places are concerned, that will all be in the past. The advantages offered by integrating housing and work stations will be that we do not have to commute back and forth and consume energy in the process. Trains, metros, light rail, shared cars and borrowed means of transportation will be prevalent everywhere. The more people per car the better. Gas stations will become recharging stations for electric cars, the first real alternative to the fossil fuel combustion engine, and later hydrogen stations for hydrogen cars. There will be electric recharging stations everywhere – in parking lots, in entrances, and near work places, so that you will always be able to recharge. Furthermore, roads, roofs, and other "city surfaces" will probably be light colored

or white, as opposed to the black roads, black roofing felt and tiles we have today. The lighter the color of the surface of the earth, the more sunlight will be reflected back into the atmosphere, just like ice does it in the arctic areas.

On the whole, our cities will become more intelligent – but in a discreet way. Every individual home will be connected to the energy network with data cables, so that the electricity company and the district heating station will be able to regulate and target their services. They may for instance regulate their production in accordance with the hours when it is cheapest to produce electricity and heat from solar, thermal, or wind generators. Your electrical appliances will switch on automatically, when the electricity is at its cheapest, for instance at night, when the windturbines are spinning. The electricity generated at this hour is less in demand and therefore cheaper. However, small decentralized units will also proliferate swiftly, for instance mini windturbines on gables and solar panels on roofs.

CATHEDRALS, SILVER BULLETS, AND OUR ABILITY TO CO-OPERATE

—

> ""
>
> # ...THE PROBLEM CAN BE SOLVED – MANY OF THE TECHNOLOGIES ARE AVAILABLE TODAY, THE POLITICAL INSTRUMENTS WE NEED ARE WELL-DEFINED AND THE COSTS [...] SEEM TO BE AFFORDABLE, EVEN IN THE PRESENT ECONOMIC CLIMATE.
>
> ""
>
> **"The Business Case for a Strong Global Deal"**
> (Copenhagen Climate Council and Climate Works 2009)
> –

In November 2008 two well-reputed American executives, Dave Rogers of the American oil company Chevron, and James Rogers, of Duke Energy, America's third largest energy supplier, spoke at a large climate convention in San Diego. The two men, who both represent the traditional energy sector, addressed the same figures and the same issues. Both expressed concern for the global warming. And yet they reached two diametrically opposed conclusions. David Rogers described the monumental, technological advances the world must embrace in just a few years in order to counter the climate crisis. He concluded that it will be an immense challenge

James Rogers also spoke from the rostrum and began by saying that in spite of the similarity in names, there is "no relation" between the Chevron and himself. The audience laughed out loud at the symbolism. James Rogers described what the US in his view should do in order to address the climate challenge. "The largest challenge in the twentieth century was the electrification of the US, ensuring that all Americans have access to electricity. In the twenty-first century we should make it our mission to de-carbonize our energy." He described how the USA must free up all its innovative powers and attempt to become the world's most energy efficient country, since this will create a considerable competitive edge.

As a listener one could not help speculating about the two diametrically opposed conclusions – and be astonished by the fact that Chevron, one of the world's largest and most influential energy companies, could be so unmotivated in terms of taking charge of the situation. What is the perspective in concluding that we cannot meet the challenge? That we should take a nap on the couch and wait for the postman to deliver the climate bill, while the world is gradually washed away outside our windows? Should we just hope the problem goes away? There seems to be only one logical approach: To begin building the type of solutions that James Rogers compares to the gigantic, awe-inspiring European cathedrals. Colossal, demanding constructions, which take generations to complete. If we lay down the foundations now, our grandchildren will be able to complete the spires.

But will it be at all possible for us to reach our goal? Reading the scientific recommendations on how to avert a major climate catastrophe can make anyone break into a cold sweat, pardon the expression. In 2050 we must have reduced the global emission of CO_2 by 50 percent. If we want to be on the safe side, we should set our sights on 85 percent. And mind you, we will have to perform this daunting task in an age, where there will be around 9 billion earthlings, and where China and India will experience a strong economic growth. In 2020 the third world will account for more than two thirds of the world's CO_2 emission.

For these reasons the challenge is twofold: We must lower the emissions of the rich world, by harvesting new clean energy sources and by improving and replacing our present technology, infrastructure and buildings. At the same time we must ensure that the poor world does not repeat our mistakes, relying on outdated polluting technologies. We must share the new technologies and ensure that the developing countries to the greatest possible extent leapfrog over the polluting phase and go directly from having no physical telephone network to establishing a mobile network, thereby circumventing the installation of material phone lines and the accompanying infrastructure. Another opportunity would be to ensure a high proportion of renewable energy at an early stage, instead of having to do a cold turkey in a few decades by cutting down on oil, coal, and gas. We could also go all out and embrace electric cars and motorbikes from the outset, as millions of people in the new global middle classes will be able to afford their own means of transportation.

If you need to calm your spirits, then fortunately you can take a look at the most advanced and thorough extrapolations concerning our technological know-how. The good news is that with present-day technologies, and those which are on the horizon, it will be possible to make the supreme effort needed to meet the challenges. The bad news is that there is no such thing as a "silver bullet", as the British say; a simple technical fix, an uncomplicated technology, which can save the world. We have to aim in many directions, focus on maximum development and application of all the technologies mentioned in the box. Then we will be able to lower the CO_2 emission in 2030 with the gigaton CO_2 recommended by science. However, this will only happen if we co-operate and share the new inventions. In return the price will be affordable – somewhere between 1-3 percent of the global gross domestic product (GDP) (read more on the interaction between climate and economy in chapter x).

However, innovation is not just about technology. We should also focus on the political framework, which creates innovation. This is patently evident in the statements made by the innovative men and women represented in this book. Do we know the traffic regulations which will allow us to take the process into overdrive?

Again the answer is yes. In numerous reports political experts have defined the tools that have proved their efficiency. For example energy standards for houses, electrical devices and consumer products, product marking conventions, goals for kilometers-per-liter-performance for cars, subsidies, dues, cheap loans for energy saving and technological co-operation between rich and poor countries.

Since he stepped down, the former British Prime Minister, Tony Blair, has – like Al Gore – applied his personal fortune and clout as former statesman in the lobby, working to create ambitious climate policies. In a 2009 report he joined forces with The Climate Group in order to analyze the connection between technological and political knowledge. And the conclusion was crystal clear: "We know that by applying seven well-tested political tools, we can achieve the reductions we need. All seven political agendas have already been applied successfully in countries around the world. Now we must disseminate them," he says.

HOW TO DO IT
—

Tony Blair points to seven well-known and simple political solutions that must be practiced globally. They will be able to solve a major part of the climate crisis, according to the study "technology for a low carbon future" (2009).
—

Of course one can choose to ignore studies and reports. However, if we are to act as enlightened human beings and base our actions on the best available knowledge, then we can only draw a rather provoking conclusion: Dave Rogers' despair should not be caused by the fact that we are *unable*, but by the fact that we are *unwilling*. As stated by the report published by the Copenhagen Climate Council and Climate Works in connection with the largest business summit leading up to COP15, World Business Summit on Climate Change in the Bella Center in May 2009: We have the technology. We have the money. We have the tools. What we need is decisions. So the question is quite simply:

Do we want to co-operate to ensure the future of the globe?

A

Energy standards for the industry
Standards for bioenergy in petrol
Energy standards for buildings
Protection against deforestation
Energy labelling of for instance fridges and televisions
Standards for renewable energy
Targets for kilometers-per-liter-performance for cars

5/20
—
THE SKY
IS THE
LIMIT

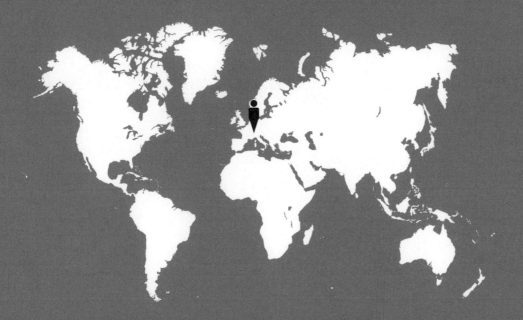

Some families bequeath generations of doctors or lawyers or farmers. For the Piccard family of Switzerland, it is explorers. Over three generations the Piccards explored the earth in every known dimension. First Auguste Piccard who in 1931 became the first human to explore the stratosphere and to see the curvature of the earth with his own eyes. Then Jacques Piccard who in 1960 reached the deepest spot in the ocean with his Bathyscaphe: 10.916 meters down into the Marianna Trench. And finally Bertrand Piccard who in March 1999, with Brian Jones, completed the first non-stop, round-the-world balloon flight. The journey took Piccard and Jones nearly 20 days and covered 45,755 kilometers. Soon after the elation of the success subsided, however,

Piccard was struck with a realization: their adventure could have failed for lack of fuel. Piccard vowed to circumnavigate the world for a second time, this time without fuel or polluting emissions.

"The grand exploits of the 20th century were conquests: the two Poles, Mt. Everest, the depths of the ocean, the Moon. Those of the 21st century, in my view, will need to consist much more of preserving, if not improving, the quality of life on our planet. How do we reconcile economic and ecological interests and promote the use of new technologies to save energy and create alternative resources?" Piccard asked as he contemplated his next adventure.

Two years later, Piccard and Jones traveled throughout the U.S. to assess the status of solar energy research and to meet with experts on solar aviation. Piccard returned to Switzerland convinced that a round-the-world flight on a manned, solar-powered aircraft was possible. A feasibility study prepared by engineers at the Ecole Polytechnique Fédérale de Lusanne (EPFL) agreed, and in November 2003, Piccard's vision, christened as Solar Impulse, was born. In 2012, Piccard will get his second chance to circle the globe when he and André Borschberg, an engineer, pilot, and the CEO of Solar Impulse, will attempt to fly around the world in the HB-SIB, a plane powered only by the sun. The trip will take Piccard and Borschberg, each flying five-day legs, 25 days of non-

1. The pilot Bertrand Piccard just after completing 25 hours of simulated flight in a small, airtight cockpit at Solar Impulse. His next flight will not be a simulation, but a five day flight in an aircraft propelled by solar power. Photo: Solar Impulse

2. André Borschberg, the co-pilot of the Solar Impulse project. Photo: Solar Impulse

1.

2.

DR. BERTRAND PICCARD (1958)

—

Is a Swiss psychiatrist and aeronaut. In 1999, he and Brian Jones completed the first non-stop, round-the-world balloon flight. Piccard and Jones set off from Château d'Oex, in Switzerland, on March 1; 19 days, 21 hours, and 47 minutes later they landed in Egypt after a 45,755-kilometer flight. Piccard descends from a long line of adventurers and inventors, including his father Jacques Piccard and grandfather Auguste Piccard, both balloonists. In addition to being the initiater of Solar Impulse, Piccard is a lecturer and a Goodwill ambassador for The United Nations.

—

stop flight. In November 2007, after four years of research, calculations, and simulations, Piccard and Borschberg presented the design of Solar Impulse's first prototype, the HB-SIA.

To keep aloft, a plane capable of flying around the world, without fuel, the project engineers came up with a design for an incredibly light, glider-like plane with a very long wingspan. The specifications are simply stunning. The wingspan, at 63.4 meters, is the same as an Airbus A340. The weight, at 1,600 kg, is the same as a small family sedan. The skeleton of the fuselage, made of light-weight but extremely strong carbon fiber, can be carried without effort by two men. The four motors powering the four propellers will generate about 10 hp each, but their average power over 24 hours is equivalent to the output of a small motorcycle, and roughly what was available to the Wright brothers when they made their maiden motorized flight in 1903. And with a top speed of 100km/h, the plane will have a hard time keeping up with the birds Piccard and Borschberg will see out the cockpit window.

So how will it stay in the air? With so little power available for its motors, the only way the plane will stay aloft is for the engineering team to have eliminated every unnecessary ounce and maximized every watt. That and batteries and solar cells – a lot of them. Nearly 12,000 super-efficient monocrystalline solar cells will be placed in sheets across the wing and horizontal stabilizer. And 400 kg of lithium batteries, twice as light as those used in cell phones, will store excess sunlight during the day.

After taking off at 35 km/h, Piccard and Borschberg will climb steadily during the day, topping out at 8,500 meters. Any higher and designers would have needed to add a pressurized cockpit, a luxury under their weight constraints. At night, the plane becomes a glider, powered by its batteries as it slowly descends to about 1,500 meters. At daybreak,

> IF AN AIRCRAFT IS ABLE TO FLY DAY AND NIGHT WITHOUT FUEL, PROPELLED ONLY BY SOLAR ENERGY, LET NO ONE CLAIM THAT IT IS IMPOSSIBLE TO DO THE SAME THING FOR MOTOR VEHICLES, HEATING AND AIR CONDITIONING SYSTEMS, AND COMPUTERS. THIS PROJECT VOICES OUR CONVICTION THAT A PIONEERING SPIRIT WITH POLITICAL VISION CAN CHANGE SOCIETY AND BRING ABOUT AN END TO FOSSIL FUEL DEPENDENCY.

the pilot will start a new ascent, as the rising sun recharges the drained batteries.

Even with the backing of engineers, and a $100-million budget, Piccard had to be prepared for a challenge all too familiar to innovators: plunging into the unknown. Solar Impulse is the most ambitious solar airplane ever made. According to Borschberg, most of the existing work on solar-powered aircraft has been for U.S. military applications such as unmanned surveillance flights with drones. He says that no aircraft has yet succeeded in flying with the HB-SIB's combination of size, weight, and speed. A ruthless commitment to efficiency was the only way forward.

"Meeting a challenge of this magnitude is possible only by taking maximum advantage of solar energy. Every watt counts, and we are looking to track down every watt we can to save energy. Only the most advanced solutions, most of them never applied before, will permit this," says Borschberg.

And then there are the near super-human demands on the pilots. Piccard and Borschberg will take turns on the final, round-the-world flight, but this still requires that they eat, sleep, and maintain the focus necessary to pilot the aircraft over five days of non-stop flying. After extensive research, Solar Impulse found that properly spaced, 20-minute naps

can prevent sleep deprivation. Not taking any chances, the pilots will be outfitted with a specially made shirt with sensors and a vibrating system that can be remotely activated to prevent them sleeping longer than 20 minutes.

In November 2009, Solar Impulse will launch the first test flights of the prototype plane, the HIB-SIA, from the Dübendorf airfield outside Zurich. If successful, in 2010 they hope to complete a 36-hour, non-stop flight to prove that a solar-powered plane can fly at night. Last, the final version of the plane, the HB-SIB, will be built in time for Piccard and Borschberg's marathon circumnavigation of the globe in 2012. For Bertrand Piccard, the fulfillment of

EXPLOITING EVERY WATT

—

With so little power available for its motors, the only way HB-SIA will stay aloft is for the engineering team to have eliminated every unnecessary ounce and fully exploited every watt. That and batteries and solar cells – a lot of them. Nearly 12,000 super-efficient monocrystalline solar cells will be placed in sheets across the wing and horizontal stabilizer. And 400 kg of lithium-ion batteries, twice as light as those used in cell phones, will store excess sunlight during the day. After taking off at 35 km/h, Piccard and Borschberg will climb steadily during the day, topping out at 8,500 meters. Any higher and designers would have needed to add a pressurized cockpit, a luxury under their weight constraints. At night, the HB-SIA becomes a glider, powered by its batteries as it slowly descends to about 1,500 meters. At daybreak, the pilots will start a new ascent, as the rising sun recharges the depleted batteries.

—

8500m

Mount Blanc

1500m

THE DRIVING FORCE BEHIND GREEN INNOVATION ACCORDING TO BERTRAND PICCARD

—

■ **The force of symbols. With its round-the-world flight, Solar Impulse hopes to offer the world a powerful symbol of the promise of renewable energy.**
■ **Every watt counts. Building a solar-powered aircraft capable of nearly perpetual flight was impossible without drastically reducing energy consumption. Solar Impulse's 70-strong engineering team, supported by some 100 researchers, has had to conceive completely new solutions to shave ounces and save watts.**

—

his vision, a decade in the making, would send a clear message to the world: "If an aircraft is able to fly day and night without fuel, propelled only by solar energy, let no one claim that it is impossible to do the same thing for motor vehicles, heating and air conditioning systems, and computers. This project voices our conviction that a pioneering spirit with political vision can together change society and bring about an end to fossil fuel dependency."

1. Several generations of sky heroes. In May 1931 Auguste Piccard, grandfather of Bertrand Piccard, flew 15.785 meters in a balloon. He set an altitude record and gathered data about the atmosphere.

2. The summer of 1932. Auguste Piccard takes to the sky in order to set new altitude records – in all he did 27 balloon flights.

1.

2.

TWO TONS
OF CO₂
PER PERSON

—

When you measure how much CO_2 an Indian, an American, and a Chinese person emits, there is great variation. An American emits twice as much CO_2 as a European, and more than five times as much as a Chinese person.

The red line indicates how much CO_2 every citizen of the world on average will be allowed to emit in 2050, if we are to prevent serious climate change - two tons of CO_2. That means that the rich world's emissions much be lowered significantly, while the drastic economic growth in the developing countries must be based on sustainable technology.

Source: The International Energy Agency (IEA)

Illustration
CO₂ emission per inhabitant in selected countries (2007).
—
The yellow mark shows the average amount of CO_2 available per person in 2050: two tons.

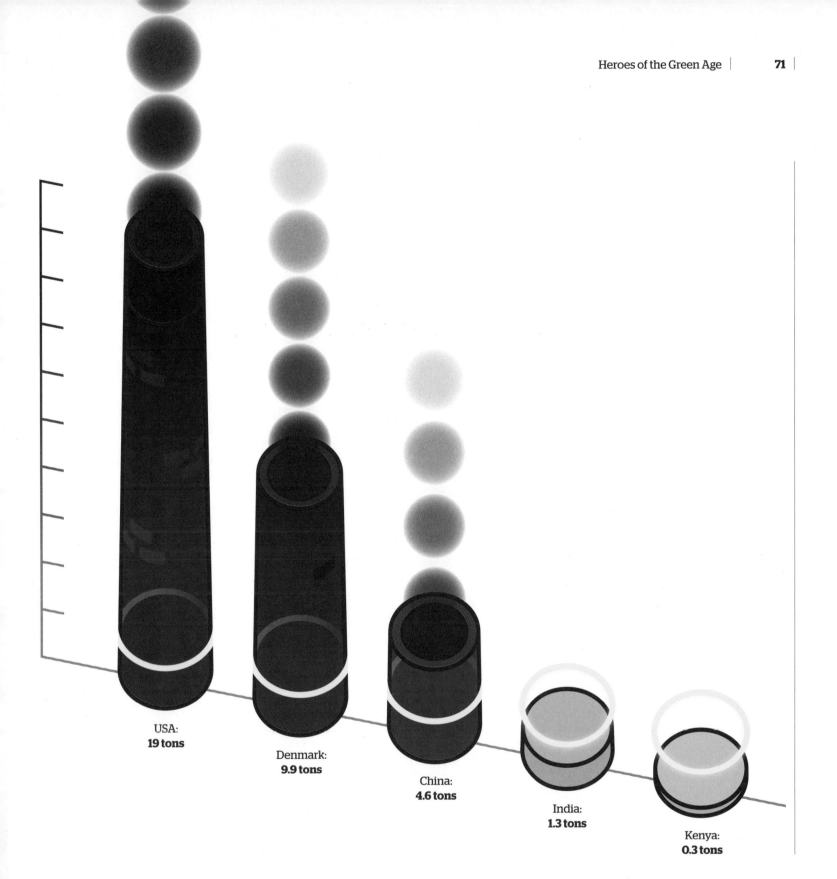

USA:
19 tons

Denmark:
9.9 tons

China:
4.6 tons

India:
1.3 tons

Kenya:
0.3 tons

6/20
—
THE MAN
OF
LIGHT
FROM
BANGALORE

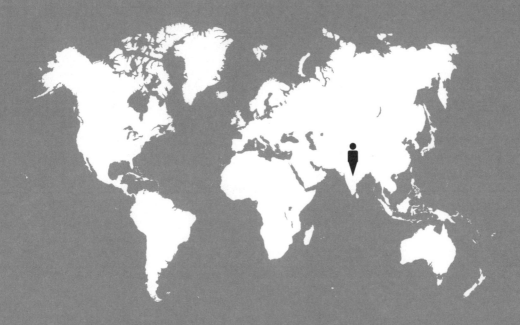

Once Bangalore was famous for its pleasant climate and green areas. However, nowadays it is neither the city parks nor the good weather that immediately meets the eye. The infernal traffic, the noise, the permanent upheaval of construction sites, and the countless office buildings in steel and glass seem to leave a greater impression. With its eight million inhabitants, Bangalore is the fastest growing city in Asia and it is known all over the world as the dynamic centre of the Indian IT industry. The city *per se* is the symbol of modern India, characterized by hectic activities, well-educated young people, advanced technology, economic growth, and a rising standard of living. The overwhelming majority of the large international IT companies have branches or head quarters in Bangalore, however, there are also

HARISH HANDE (1968)

—

Grew up in a privileged home in the constituent state of Orissa. He was educated at the Indian Institute of Technology, IIT, and has a Ph.D. in Solar Energy from the University of Massachusetts. He has received a number of prizes and distinctions, most recently the Financial Times Boldness in Business Award in 2009.

—

many other companies whose most important resources are a highly qualified work force and specialized knowledge. One of the companies is Solar Light Private Limited.

Selco Solar Light was founded in 1995 by Dr. Harish Hande, the managing director of the company. The young Hande was motivated to set up Selco by the fact that almost half the population of India does not have access to electricity. Solar energy was his solution. He wished to offer the poor people in the country individual solutions so they could get decent lighting, and possibly also energy to run small machines such as sewing machines and handlooms. Solar panels and solar energy are a cheap solution for the poor people who live

in the enormous slums without electricity and in rural areas off the grid and far from power plants. Solar energy is cheaper than their fossil fuels, mainly kerosene, but also cheaper than expensive non-rechargeable batteries - the kind they have to use when darkness falls.

Today, Selco has sold more than 110,000 solar plants and the company has 26 branches in the south of India with more than 170 employees. However, nobody could have foreseen that the privileged Harish Hande was to become a pioneer bringing solar energy to the poor. Least of all himself. "I had a sheltered upbringing in the constituent state Orissa. I studied Energy Engineering at the Indian Institute of Technology, and in

1990 I travelled to the USA to get a Ph.D.," says Harish Hande.

The following year, he visited the Dominican Republic, where he noticed that many poor people had solar panels on their roofs. And this turned the young Indian's life upside down. "I felt wretched because of the fact that I had not even considered what it is like for a great number of my compatriots to live without electricity. I finally went to Sri Lanka to experience for myself what it would be like. I deliberately did not go to a poor village in India. An educated, privileged man like me would never be treated as an equal there," Harish Hande explains. Having graduated with a Ph.D. in solar energy in the U.S., he

1.

and an American colleague got the idea for a company that sells solar energy to the poorest people in the world.

In Haris Hande's opinion, poverty is one of the greatest threats, but can we ask a poor woman not to chop wood and use it for her stove? Or not to use kerosene in her lamp? No... Instead we must create alternatives for her, he thinks. However, the idea of bringing solar energy to the poor was not an instant success among the investors and in the business world. The arguments against this industry were many. Solar plants are unreliable, the poor cannot afford them and much less figure out how to operate and maintain them. In general, most people doubted that a company

could be run on commercial terms with poor people as its customer base. Nevertheless, Selco succeeded; mainly because the idea is sustainable – and Harish Hande and his colleagues do not expect to make excessive amounts of money.

The employees do not spend much time on the solar technology itself. They buy Indian standard components – a solar panel, one or two batteries, wires, switches, and hook-ups. Then they create a custom made solution for the individual buyer and her needs. Selco also has another custom-made simple idea that has made life easier for many people in India. It is a headlight that runs on a small solar battery. Every night, small armies of rose pickers wan-

SOLAR ENERGY TO THE POOR

—

Almost half of the Indian population does not have access to electricity. Since 1994 Selco has sold 110,000 solar plants to poor Indians in the slums and rural areas. The plants typically generate electricity for 4-6 light bulbs per home and/or a sewing machine or another small machine. To the poorest Indians, who do not live in areas with access to electricity, solar plants are a cheap solution – cheaper than the kerosene, which they have burnt in their lamps so far. The environmental savings are also considerable. A family typically uses around 120 liters of kerosene to light up their home every year, and 110,000 solar plants prevent the emission of 33,000 tons of CO_2 on an annual basis. In addition to private homes, Selco has also supplied smaller businesses, street vendors, public institutions, temples, etc. with solar plants. The goal is to reach 200,000 users in the next four years.

—

1. A solar panel on the roof provides light to the poorest people. It gives them the opportunity to prolong their working day, and it allows their children to read in the evening.

1.

**THE DRIVING FORCE BEHIND
GREEN INNOVATION ACCORDING TO
HARISH HANDE**
—
■ **The product and the technology
must be adjusted to the needs of the
user.**
■ **Investing in sustainable solutions
should improve the customer's life
and/or economy.**
—

der into the fields in the rural districts. In the cool darkness they pick roses, which are sent to the daily markets. In the old days they used to pick with one hand, while they held a kerosene lamp in the other. Now, they strap the new lamp on their forehead and pick with both hands. When the sun rises they recharge the batteries in the solar plant in their home. The small headlight is also used by midwives and doctors who previously had to work in darkness or by kerosene lamps that every year cause severe burns and claim the lives of children and adults.

A typical plant which produces enough electricity for four lamps in a home costs around 10,000 rupees or approx. 200 dollars. To many poor Indians this represents several yearly wages. However, many buyers simply use their new light to prolong their working hours and cottage industries, thereby making more money. They can sew more clothes, do more basket work, pick more roses or roll more *beedis* – small hand rolled cigarettes that are smoked everywhere in India. The income

1. Women sorting betel nuts.

from the expanded production plus the amounts saved on kerosene and batteries is sufficient to make the solar energy investment a profitable business. At the same time, there are also considerable environmental advantages. The small homes will not be subjected to dangerous kerosene smoke and the CO_2 emission will be reduced. A family uses approx. 120 liters of kerosene per year on lamps. This means that the 110,000 installed plants prevent the emission of 33,000 tons of CO_2 every year. The calculation takes into account the fact that it costs CO_2 to produce the plants.

Even if Hande and his co-workers encountered skepticism during the first years, Selco has achieved official recognition in the form of a number of prizes. In several cases they included funds for the development of the company such as the Tech Awards in 2005, the Social Entrepreneur of the Year Award 2007, and the Financial Times Boldness in Business Award 2009. "The recognition has been important to us for several reasons. Among other things, it meant that I was invited to the World Economic Forum summit in Davos, which is a very good place to meet decision-makers. It is

relatively easy to meet European and American decision-makers, while it is extremely difficult to set up a meeting with anyone from India," says Harish Hande. He is convinced that solar technology will improve and become cheaper in the coming years. Nevertheless, he is a climate pessimist. "Climate change continue because we are not serious about fighting them. We need a completely different approach if we want to create an effect. That will take a considerable change of attitude and apparently we are not ready for that yet," says Harish Hande.

THE THIRD WORLD IN THE FAST LANE

—

Electric cars remind most people of Toyota, Tesla – or golf cars. However, China and India are on the cutting edge of technology related to new sustainable cars. The Chinese electric car is called BYD – Build Your Dream – and is produced by the world's greatest manufacturer of batteries for mobile phones. A BYD has a range of around 100 kilometers before the battery must be recharged – and if you have access to an electrical outlet, you can recharge overnight. In a special outlet it takes little more than 15 minutes. The battery can be recharged indefinitely, usually needing complete replacement after 500.000 kilometers. The BYD car is a hybrid car. It can switch to a petrol motor, if the battery is depleted. The BYD is also on its way to Europe.

In India they have the Reva, the world's bestselling electric car. It is a small family car designed for a couple and two young children. It runs exclusively on electricity, and it is cheap and easy to maneuver in the chaotic Indian cities. It has a top speed of 70-80 kilometers per hour, but mostly it stays around 20 kilometers per hour, the average speed in the busy streets. The Reva is also available in Europe and in the coming years the factory plans on introducing new innovative models, among them a hydrogen car. So far there are around 2000 Revas in the world.

1. EA Chinese dream - a BYD car.
2. A small, Indian car - the Reva.

1.

2.

7/20
—
LET THE SUNSHINE IN

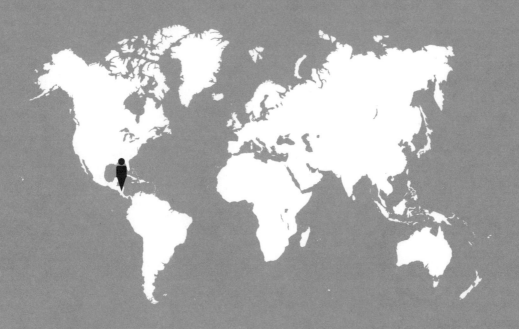

It is noon in Managua, the capital of Nicaragua. The sun shines relentlessly from a clear blue sky and the thermometer says 38 degrees in the shade. In most offices, shops, and in private homes the air condition is humming on full power, fighting an endless battle for a more bearable temperature. This is not the way in Max Lacayo's office. He is the director of the family owned company ECAMI, which produces affordable alternative energy plants. "We mainly use fans in our office. They keep the temperature down and for a couple of hours a day we switch on our air condition. Of course we supply some of the electricity with our own solar panels," Max Lacayo explains and nods towards a display of solar panels, batteries, wind turbines and water tanks. Max Lacayo and ECAMI sell renewable energy –

MAX LACAYO (1985)

—

Born in Nicaragua. He trained as a lawyer and specialized in company law. At the moment he is completing a master's degree in renewable energy. In 2005 he took over the daily management of the family owned company ECAMI, which his father founded in 1982, shortly after the Nicaraguan revolution. Today ECAMI sells and installs wind and solar plants in the Central American country. A substantial number of the customers are located in remote areas of the country, which are not yet on the grid. In 2009 ECAMI was awarded the prestigious Ashden Award for its support of the development in the Nicaraguan rural areas.

—

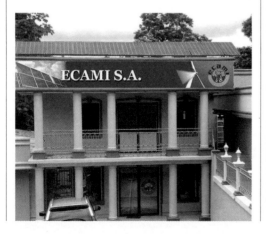

primarily solar energy – in a country which is particularly suited for this.

"Here in Nicaragua we are on average able to harness five hours of maximum level solar energy per day. In Germany, for instance, you have on average three hours. In Nicaragua the conditions are ideal. In the countryside, we install plants for the production of electricity. For those who already have electricity it is not a great bonus since we simply cannot produce enough to make a difference. But for those who are off the grid it is a colossal opportunity," says Max Lacayo and leans forward in the chair. Now we get to a matter close to his heart: "It is impressive how much one watt can mean to people who do not have any electricity. To 40 percent of the population in this country it would not matter if we expanded the central supply since they have no access to electricity. However, with a solar panel and a battery 100 watts can make a world of difference to them. They can watch television and listen to the radio, keep themselves informed, recharge their cell phones, call the hospital when they need to, and their children can do their homework in the evening," Max Lacayo explains. He has travelled all over Nicaragua to install the plants.

When ECAMI brings solar panels and equipment to people in remote trackless areas, they often have to undertake the journey on stony mountainsides on a donkey. Nicaragua is an impassable country and the roads do not extend very far into the country. Tall mountain ranges, enormous fertile lowlands and tropical rainforests characterize the countryside, where every fourth citizen has a dollar or less to live on per day. The solar panels are installed on the roofs of the peasants' houses and are connected to a rechargeable battery so the energy can be stored and used night and day. The battery is automatically disconnected from the solar panel when it is fully charged, so that it does not burn out.

The ECAMI people install wires and contacts in the house so the families can get electric light, switch on the radio and television, and charge their mobile phone. "ECAMI is a private company which must make a profit. However, our plant actually also has a social purpose. I usually say that we have three results on the bottom line, when we install a solar energy plant in a farmer's house. The family will generate smaller bills for fossil fuel such as petroleum – a result with an environmental and an economic impact. However, the social consequences should also enter into the equation, since it increases their quality of life to have access to just a small amount of electricity," says Max Lacayo.

Nicaragua is one of the poorest countries in Latin America, only Haiti is poorer. There are many pressing needs and Max Lacayo is well aware that renewable energy is not a priority of the authorities. He says that ECAMI constantly fights to get the energy agenda integrated into the public debate. However, the authorities turn a deaf ear while insisting on very high taxes and import duty on the solar panels. However, this challenge is nothing compared to the conditions, which faced ECAMI when the company started up in 1982.

"The revolution was just over and the communication lines in the country were severed. My father is a radio technician and he had the idea that the peasants could communicate with walkie-talkies. But how would they charge the batteries? They used car engines, but that was too troublesome and one day he read in a magazine that they could use solar panels. At the time this was quite new in Cen-

LIGHT FOR THE PEOPLE
—

**ECAMI was founded in 1982 for the purpose of improving the communication in the rural areas after the revolution. The peasants were not able to recharge their walkie talkies, so for this reason ECAMI began importing solar panels for electricity production. In the beginning of the 1990s ECAMI introduced thermal systems, where the solar panels heat water and since then they have added small wind turbines. ECAMI has installed around 9000 solar panels in 5000 plants in all of Nicaragua. The panels installed have a capacity of 600 kilowatt. In later years alone the capacity has increased by 200 kilowatt. ECAMI employs 35 workers. The company's customers are primarily located in remote areas of Nicaragua.
In principle a solar plant for a one family house consists of a solar panel on the roof attached to a rechargeable battery, allowing for the use of electricity night and day. ECAMI installs the plant and mounts switches in the house for light, radio, television and cell phone chargers. Furthermore, ECAMI demonstrates to the new owners of the solar panels how they should maintain and eventually carry out small repairs.**
—

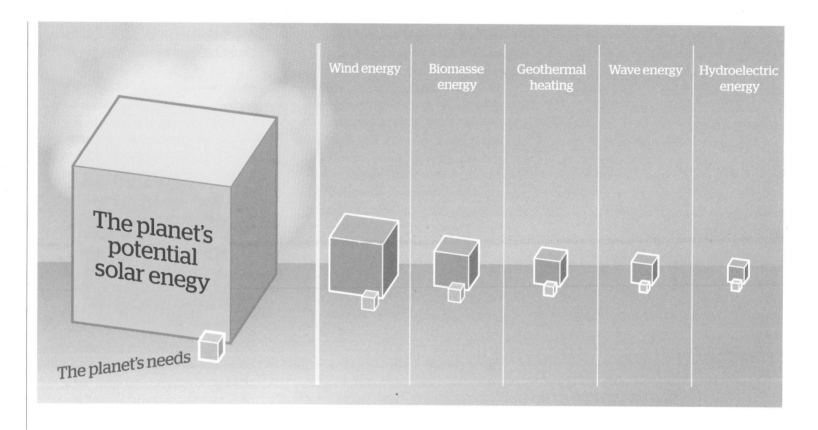

Wind energy | Biomasse energy | Geothermal heating | Wave energy | Hydroelectric energy

The planet's potential solar enegy

The planet's needs

tral America and he had no knowledge about it. Still, he forged ahead and imported some plants. By the time the first plant had been installed, he realized that the solar panels could also be used to generate light," Max Lacayo explains.

Later ECAMI became aware of the opportunities represented by wind energy. In the future the company also aims to make better use of thermal solar energy applied in the heating of water. The customers are both private home owners and hotels – a hotel in the capital may supply 100 rooms with hot water via thermal solar energy alone. The environmental savings are substantial and Max Lacayo's climate consciousness is growing.

"We contribute to the CO_2 balance with substantial savings on the running of mobile radio masts in remote areas. Previously they were run by diesel generators, but with solar panels we can reduce the fossil fuel consumption for every mast with 54,000 liters of diesel per year. We also work hard to install a solar driven stove in order to reduce the deforestation in the country. So several things are happening," says Max Lacayo.

"I love my job. I meet many people and see how they live in the country far from our urban comfort. Their day ends at six p.m., when the sun goes down, so out there you really learn to appreciate energy. It is wonderful to see how that makes a difference in their

lives. In a co-operation with UNICEF we have installed solar panels on the roofs of health clinics, so they have electric light available, when servicing patients after sunset. Furthermore, the electricity enables them to run a fridge to keep the vaccines cool and children with breathing problems can be helped with oxygen masks," Lacayo explains. He also takes the energy situation on the home front seriously. "Naturally we have solar panels for electricity, as well as water heating and I would like to manage completely without the public electricity supply, but that is not possible. Not even if we use LED lighting and energy saver light bulbs," Lacayo sighs – without reason though. He is already demonstrating a much greater

**THE DRIVING FORCE BEHIND
GREEN INNOVATION ACCORDING TO
MAX LACAYO**

—

■ The work I do creates change. Giving people access to electric light makes a difference in their lives.
■ Every single watt we install contributes to the reduction of climate change.

—

climate consciousness than most other Nicaraguans. The country is fertile, but poor, so only a minority of the population thinks twice about the consumption of resources in the daily struggle to survive. For this reason, among others, Max Lacayo feels that it is important that people should own their own solar plants and develop an understanding of how they function technically."This project must be sustainable. The plants we install are often located hundreds of kilometers away from the cities, so they must function well. Equipment and installation must be in order, but people should also be capable of repairing the plants, when necessary. It is no good that the plants stop because a 50 cent fuse has blown. So we always teach people how the plants function and explain the limitations of the plants, so they use the energy with care. In the beginning the children will typically play with the light or watch television for hours on end and then the battery will be flat. One must understand the limitations of the system. Otherwise the result will just be frustration," says Max Lacayo.

SKYSCRAPER
FARMING

—

At the moment a fast growing number of green architects are doing experiments, developing buildings and urban areas with a view to taking on the climate challenge. They look e.g. the fact that a growing proportion of the world's population lives in large cities. In 2050 it is expected that three out of four citizens of the world will be big city dwellers. Actually that is more of an opportunity than a problem. It is easier to make densely populated areas energy efficient, both in terms of housing and transport. The architects attempt to integrate plants and trees in the buildings of the future, because they absorb CO_2 and make the buil-

dings more attractive. An example is *Bosco Verticale*, two skyscrapers in Milan, which combine trees, windturbines, and housing. In all, the buildings house 10.000 square meters of forest.

Some architects and city planners experiment with city farming in skyscrapers, so-called "vertical farms". In fact the American group of Architects Mithun has designed a skyscraper farm in Seattle with room for fields with vegetables and grains, greenhouses and even a chicken farm – combined with 318 apartments. The construction is self-sustainable with regard to energy and water.

Pictures
Green heights. Design sketches by the American architectural, entrepreneurial and city planning company Mitchun in Seattle.

8/20

—

THE SOAP BUBBLE MAN

"A box full of soap bubbles" is how Tristram Carfrae describes his eccentric, beautiful blue-green building in Beijing, the capital of China. He developed the idea behind The Water Cube, Beijing's national water sports stadium, and built it in co-operation with a dream team of specialized architects and engineers, selected for their knowledge about steel, light, acoustics, and installation, as well as advisers and construction workers. The building was completed in time for the Beijing Olympics in 2008.

In the catalogue of buildings designed by Tristram Carfrae, the Water Cube yields the best response to his expectations in terms of sustainability. "We were a team of specialists, who joined forces and created a fantastic structure. It is self-sufficient with regard to light and heat, it reclaims and cleans grey

TRISTRAM CARFRAE (1959)
—

Grew up in Great Britain and lives and works in Sydney, Australia. He is a civil engineer specializing in structural design. He has a leading position on Arup's global board. Arup is one of the world's leading engineering companies in the field of sustainable solutions and construction. The company employs around 9,000 people worldwide. Tristram Carfrae's expertise is to blend the right type of construction with a suitable aesthetic expression. He has constructed many sports facilities and stadiums. Besides the Water Cube in Beijing, Tristram Carfrae has fostered several prize winning projects in Great Britain and Australia. In 2001, he was appointed engineer of the year in Australia and in 2005, the Australian Association of Engineers elected him one of the 100 most influential engineers in Australia.
—

water, and the sound is amazing. It is earth quake resistant – fortunately this has not yet been tested. A minimum of materials were used in the construction. Furthermore, it is captivating, beautiful, and spiritually enlightening," says Tristram Carfrae who works for the engineering company Arup, which has a leading edge in sustainable constructions and solutions.

In sustainable building there is added focus on the materials applied. It is important to use as few materials as possible, since their production and transport should consume as little energy and create as few waste products as possible. The materials should preferably be recycled or at least recyclable. A sustainable building should be well-insulated and consume a modest amount of – renewable – energy for heating, cooling, air condition, light and water. The sustainable building should be pleasant to be in. If a public building, it should be easy to reach without a car for instance. At the same time, it should address the needs of a majority of people, and not just a select circle. It should also be pleasant to look at, according to Tristram Carfrae.

Tristram Carfrae is British and lives and works in Australia. We meet him in New York City, where he is between flights *en route* to San Francisco. He is a civil engineer specializing in structural design, a member of Arup's global management board, and leading employee in the company, which employs 9,000 people worldwide.

In spite of its tender age, the box of soap bubbles in Beijing has already become a landmark. Hu Jintao, the president of China, has lauded the Ice Cube as a model design for China's future development – the skies of China must be clearer, the countryside greener, and the water cleaner. The Chinese swimming stadium consists of a steel construction. A thick plastic film or membrane is suspended above the construction. The plastic membrane is divided into small inflated cells that look like

THE WATER CUBE:

—

The Water Cube looks blue, but is in fact green. The building is 177 meters long, 177 meters wide, and 31 meters high. It has 17,000 seats and several pools. It consists of a minimum of construction materials. The construction is covered by a thin lightweight foil. The blue foil with the many bubbles gives the impression of bubbles in water. Obviously, the architects in the Australian company PTW, who designed the building, desired this effect. Every bubble or cell can be replaced individually, if necessary. The foil or membrane is a type of plastic covered in Teflon. It is called EFTE and was originally developed by the aviation industry. Hence it is a lightweight material. It is made from recycled materials and can be melted and recycled again. The membrane functions as a large surface of solar panels and can be applied to heat the pools. The Water Cube operates in line with the greenhouse principle – the sunlight penetrates the membrane and there is constant ventilation. According to Arup's own calculations, the design will save at least thirty percent energy on heating and lighting. All construction materials have been carefully selected with a view to environmentally friendly parameters. And the price? Approx. 200 million dollars.

—

THE DRIVING FORCE BEHIND
GREEN INNOVATION ACCORDING TO
TRISTRAM CARFRAE
—
■ "We should begin by weighing expenses against societal advantages.
Consumption, CO_2 emission, and
economy should be juxtaposed with
the advantages which sustainable
solutions can give society as a whole."
■ "We must stop thinking only in
terms of economy and what 'pays off'.
We run the risk of losing our soul and
make the world a worse place to be."
—

soap bubbles. The building is lightweight and
weighs a fraction of what a similar building in
glass or steel would weigh. The membrane is
made out of renewable materials that can be
melted and recycled. Furthermore, it is much
cheaper than a glass dome.

The membrane catches the sunlight and
functions like solar cells which contribute to
the heating of the pools in the stadium, while
the daylight penetrates the shell and creates
a pleasant light without the use of energy.
The Water Cube is an experiment – nothing
like it has ever been seen before. If buildings,
bridges, neighborhoods, and entire cities are to
be built with sustainable technology, there will
be a great need for experiments and alternative thinking. "I believe that one of the greatest
future challenges will be to convince my archi-
tect colleagues that it is possible to construct
beautiful houses and areas without squander-
ing raw materials and producing excessive
amounts of waste. The need for decent urban

> **I DOUBT THAT HUMANITY CAN KEEP ITS HANDS OFF THE LARGE QUANTITIES OF OIL AND GAS STILL LODGED UNDERGROUND. IT IS QUITE SIMPLY TOO EASY TO GO OVERBOARD AND USE EXCESSIVE AMOUNTS OF OIL AND GAS.**

planning in developing countries will double in the course of the next 40 years. It will soon be crystal clear that we have to spend less energy and fewer materials than we do at present. However, unfortunately the present trend is to build houses that need greater amounts of advanced material," Tristram Carfrae states. His own interest in green construction began towards the end of the 1990s, when a colleague graduated with a PhD in the exotic subject of sustainable cities. "I was immediately fascinated and captivated by the holistic aspect of the principle of sustainability – to build with consideration for the environment, while also taking social and economic aspects into account. Till then I had not been convinced by the environmental movement. There was too much of the 'knit your own yogurt' attitude for my taste, and I failed to see how that could save the world," says Tristram Carfrae.

He realizes that there is no way around major immediate investments in sustainable energy solutions, especially in the developing countries. That will necessitate economic support from the industrialized countries. At the same time, Tristram Carfrae doubts that humanity can keep its hands off the large amounts of oil and gas still lodged underground.

"It is quite simply too easy to go overboard and use excessive quantities of oil and gas. Such an approach will continue to generate large amounts of greenhouse gasses, so I trust that humanity will be able to develop a type of CO_2 filtration technique in the course of the next 50 years. Research into this area should really be supported and encouraged," says the engineer. Tristram Carfrae is a true optimist: "I believe that we will overcome this crisis. We will find a way to delimit the climate change and adapt to the new climate we have created. We will reduce poverty and make the world a better place," says Tristram Carfrae. "We will work it out."

—

**"It was quite a disappointment,
to put it mildly,"** says Curtis Felix.
He takes a quick sip of his beer and scans
the room, as if looking for an answer.
Earlier in the year the energy expert from
Massachusetts had secured a 20 million
US dollar investment in his algae energy
project. Then the financial crisis struck,
and the investment did not eventuate.
**"At the moment it is incredibly difficult
to raise money. We hope that the
government will grant us money,
but if not..."**

—

⋮

He looks like a man who is on
the verge of throwing in the towel.
For a number of years he has fought for his
project, proved that it works, and now the
customers are ready. All he needs is to cover
the last distance between experiment and
pilot project – the most difficult phase.
**"The last resort will be to mortgage my
house, so I will probably do that,
if necessary,"** he says with renewed energy,
telling the whole story of how he
built the house himself and fitted it with
solar panels, because he is certain that
one day new buyers will agree with
him that it would be the only
right thing to do.

—

9/20
—
THE ELECTRIC CAR **GURU**

Like the Blues Brothers, Israeli American Shai Agassi is on a mission for sustainable cars. He wants to "wean us off oil" by combining cars with solar and wind energy, thereby creating a transport system driven by "clean electrons". This could bring about a definitive end to our dependence on oil and petrol. He has compared oil to heroin and says that the shift from oil to solar and wind is the equivalent of a junkie going from heroin to milk. The idea is based on electric family cars, whose renewable batteries will be recharged with energy from solar farms and windturbine parks. The preparations have reached an advanced stage in Israel, Australia, Canada, Portugal, and Denmark in co-operation with large, local energy companies and car manufacturers, such as Renault/Nissan. In 2009, the first cars

SHAI AGASSI (1968)

—

Was born in Ramat Gan in Israel. At the age of 21, he completed an education in computer science at Technion, the Israeli Institute of Technology. Until 2007, he was the leader of the product and technology sector at SAP, one of the world's leading software companies, which he left, when he founded Better Place. In 2003, the TV station CNN appointed him one of the world's twenty leading "Global Influentials", and in 2009 he was on *Time Magazine's* list of the 100 most influential people in the world. Better Place is based in Israel as well as in California.

—

based on Shai Agassi's ideas were introduced in Denmark.

You would have a difficult time finding a more staunch personification of a global, green paradigm shift. The 41-year-old Shai Agassi has raised around one billion US dollars for the project, and he is convinced that he is well on the way to creating "the future of the car". He is so convinced that the media-blitz he has spun during the last couple of years, has earned him nicknames that span from "the guru" to "the evangelist". In 2008, The New York Times columnist Thomas L. Friedman called him "the Jewish Henry Ford" and predicted that Shai Agassi would start an energy revolution. When you meet Shai Agassi, you tend to agree. He is an eloquent, direct and convincing man, whether he is on a

REFUEL WITH WIND AND SUN

–

The Better Places concept is inspired by the cell phone. The customers purchase an electric car and subscribe to the batteries, which can be recharged at charging stations located in parking lots and near homes. The batteries can also be renewed at service stations, where they will automatically be replaced by a recharged battery - all in a two-minute operation. Every lithium ion battery has a range of approx. 160 kilometers and is reusable. The cars are traditional family cars. The first cars were made by Renault/Nissan and became available in 2009 in Denmark and Israel. In Israel, the electricity is supplied by solar energy farms in the Negev Desert. In Denmark, the batteries are to be recharged overnight by excess electricity from wind turbines. New projects are on the way in Australia, Portugal, Ontario, Canada, and in San Francisco, USA.

–

conference panel with thousands of listeners, on television, or face to face. If anyone can sell sand in the Sahara or electric cars in a petrol loving world, it would be Shai Agassi.

"At the moment, we are experiencing a boom in innovation. There is an abundance of young business people with smart ideas. I believe that the generation of business people, who have become rich at a relatively young age, think forty years ahead and have made up

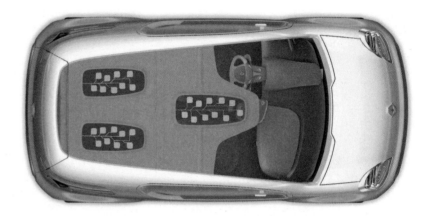

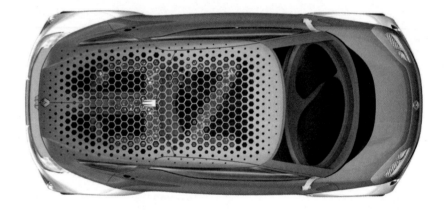

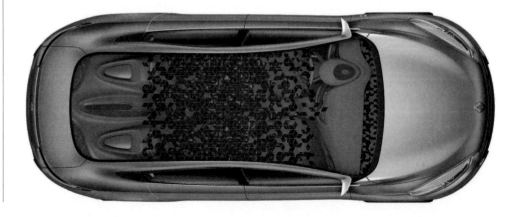

their minds that they are not interested in creating a new Facebook or Twitter. They want to solve some of the problems which have a serious effect on society."

"In 2020, we will look back at this age and think: Wow! That was one of the most impressive phases in human innovation. It will be compared to the last decade of the nineteenth century and the first decade of the twentieth century, when Edison, Westinghouse, and Tesla among other things invented the lightbulb, the pneumatic brake, and the alternating current, respectively. Those guys and other contemporary scientists innovated our society and changed our media, communication, and transport system," says Agassi. His personal turning point came in 2007 during a conversation with Simon Peres, then president of Israel. "Peres said to me: 'Israel will realize your project, if you provide the money and the cars.' Then he said: 'Just come to Israel and do it.' Then you do not have a choice. When your president asks you to fulfil your obligations to your country and the world, then you do it. I immediately realized that this was more important than anything else I could do," says Shai Agassi, who astonished everybody by leaving a job as second in command in the German IT giant SAP, prior to becoming the chief executive. He thereby also personifies the change in mentality of the leading young entrepreneurs' who in recent years have shifted their focus from high tech to green tech. Shai Agassi is very interested in being instrumental, when it comes to changing other people's minds. "I would want to attract the best innovators to this market. For this reason we do our best to show what we are doing. We want to demonstrate that it is not just about goodwill, but also good business. We must put all the big brains to work and if they do that, if we use the brain power out there, then I am convinced that we can solve this problem as well as even larger problems," says Agassi, who began his higher education in computer science at the age of 15.

As opposed to many of his colleagues, Shai Agassi does not believe in CO_2 quotas and global agreements as the driving forces behind innovation. "I support concrete bans and mandated regulations. Governments must be able to use force as a strategy and make up their minds about concrete solutions. Electric lightbulbs with heat loss must be prohibited, as well as leaking windows and exhaust pipes. Reductions alone will not do the trick. Mandate change. That will be the only effective means," says Shai Agassi, who also firmly believes that one should always place the customer at the centre of the process.

Electric cars must be fantastic to drive, and energy saver bulbs must provide good light. Otherwise, we might just as well forget all about it.

IF YOU'RE N
EVERY NOW
IT'S A SIC
NOT DOING AI
INNOV

Woody Allen,
Director

OT FAILING
AND AGAIN,
N YOU'RE
YTHING VERY
ATIVE

0 KILOMETERS IN 100 YEARS

The combustion engine is a thought-provoking example of how desperately we need innovation. In 1908, when Henry Ford drove the first Ford T from the assembly line into the street, it did around ten kilometers per liter. In 2008, one hundred years later, the average American car does approx. 8,5 kilometers per liter. Of course present-day cars drive faster and are fitted with air-bags, radio, and air-condition – but the technique is basically the same.

Source: The American Environmental Protection Agency (EPA) and The Detroit News.

1.

1. Ford today.
2. Ford T, ca. 1908

2.

10/20
—
ISLE OF
PLENTY

When the ferry approaches Samsø, the first sight that meets the eye are the white wind turbines contrasted by the deep blue sea. Ten enormous wind turbines are positioned in the waves along the island's coastline. On the island white wings of the wind turbines reach towards the sky along with church towers and the old lighthouse on the southernmost tip. The small, isolated and windblown island in the centre of Kattegat and in the centre of Denmark is a rare success story about the renewable energy that the world needs right now. The island was formerly known throughout the country for producing the first spring crops of potatoes and for its sweet strawberries. Today the inhabitants have abandoned oil and coal fired energy, and are embracing clean energy sources such as sun, wind, and

> **IF AN ENGINEER IN A SUIT AND TIE ARRIVES FROM THE CAPITAL AND TELLS YOU TO BUILD A WIND TURBINE ON FARMER JENSEN'S FIELD, THEN THE LOCALS WOULD BALK AT SUCH A TOP-DOWN APPROACH.**

bales of straw. This initiative has brought them worldwide praise and recognition as green role models. Students, politicians and experts from far corners of the world are flocking to the green island to learn from the Danish adventure. Television crews from CNN, ZDF and China TV are almost tripping over each other in their eagerness to tell the climate story of "yes, we can!"

During the last ten years the small island community of little more than 4000 souls has become self-sufficient in heat and electricity generated by wind turbines and other renewable energy sources. The island's next priority area is waste management and ecology, as well as the sore spot: transport.

The island is indebted to one man, who is the catalyst and the prime mover in the cre-

ation of this success story: Søren Hermansen, farmer, environmental technician and now the director of the Samsø Energy Academy. He is short, stocky, and tanned and he greets you with a big smile. During the last eleven years he has performed the long haul from the first skeptical public meetings about wind turbines, and today the politicians are standing in line to pad him on the shoulder.

"Yes, I believe that a process is often initiated because of one person's will and enthusiasm. This is not specific to Samsø and I – one can observe this phenomenon in other locations where the environment is suddenly in focus because of a person who has a central position. On Samsø that person happened to be me," says Søren Hermansen, attempting to play down his own role in the project. In

Denmark humility is a virtue. "My drive probably originates from the old fashioned farming community, from my time as a farmer. I was the type of farmer who felt that nature should be an integrated circuit – that you cannot just endlessly consume the fields, the animals, and the resources. You must reciprocate. However, of course I am not alone in this venture to transform Samsø to an island of renewable energy. Innovation must be contagious," says Søren Hermansen.

In 1997 the Danish government set up a competition in order to find the Danish island which had the most advanced approach to renewable energy. The islands were to present a ten year plan of how to establish renewable energy through well established technologies, local enthusiasm and drive, and little or no subsidies from the state. The winning island was to function as a "distinctive national showcase" for Danish environmental technology. The objective was twofold: to promote alternative sources of energy – and create new life and growth on the Danish islands which even today are threatened by depopulation. The plan submitted by Samsø won the competition. Everyone was proud. All they had to do now was put the plan into practice. And that turned out to be more difficult than making it.

Søren Hermansen was there form the word go. As the first employee on the Samsø project, he was hired on a part time basis to inform and give advice. To him it was not just a job. "I must admit I had a vision. A vision of Samsø as a greener and cleaner island," says Søren Hermansen eleven years later. Søren Hermansen refers to his original occupation, stressing some of the social qualities of the traditional farming community. In the traditional communities you felt responsibility for the local community and pooled your efforts to solve practical problems. Søren Hermansen has been able to revive this quality on Samsø with the purpose of introducing clean technology in several fields.

"We got a good piece of advice from the engineering company which helped in the construction of the ambitious energy plan. They told us to include the local population right from the start. If an engineer in a suit and tie arrives from the capital and tells you to build a wind turbine on farmer Jensen's field, then the locals would balk at such a top-down approach. That would be the attitude on Samsø – and in most other places. The momentum should come from the local community," says Søren Hermansen. It is his great inspirational idea and his most important piece of advice:

SØREN HERMANSEN (1959)
—

Grew up on Samsø. He took over the family farm and has supplemented his education with training in environmental techniques. Today, he is the manager of the Samsø Energy Academy, an institution that gives advice on energy conservation and renewable energy. Furthermore, the Samsø Energy Academy mediates knowledge about the Samsø project. Every year, the Academy services a couple of thousand visiting journalists, students, and NGOs. Søren Hermansen has won countless prizes for his work, most recently "The Green Nobel Prize", the prestigious Swedish Gothenburg Prize (Göteborgprisen).
—

such a venture must have anchorage in a popular movement and consultations with the citizens. The first year consisted mainly of meetings. Søren Hermansen attended all conceivable public meetings. In the approximately 30 smaller and larger villages and towns on the island there were meetings about e.g. licensed sale of alcohol in cafes and pubs, a subject that could bring in a large crowd. When the debate about licenses was dying out, Søren Hermansen would pop up with a comment: "Excuse me, I would like to tell you all something about alternative energy. There are advantages in installing solar panels on the rooftops of the farms. And of course wind turbines ..."

In fact that is the second piece of advice: people should know what the advantages are – and the amount of money they can save – by embracing alternative energy. "When the first straw-fired burners have been installed on a farm and the neighbors and others in the village realize that it works and that the farmer saves money – well, then the ball is rolling and others want to get involved. That is what happened here," says Søren Hermansen. After the first year the project took off. A large convention was arranged where vendors of heat pumps, solar panels, and new technology arrived on Samsø. The local skilled laborers acquired new competences and began negotiating and installing the new technology and erecting the first wind turbines. There was no opposition against wind turbines as such, only against their placing. "The neighbor's wind turbine is ugly. It ruins your view. However, if you yourself own a part of it and get cheap electricity from it, then it suddenly looks somewhat better," says Søren Hermansen and shrugs. That is just the way it is.

Today there are eleven wind turbines on Samsø. They are one of the many results of the effort which *The New Yorker* has labeled: "...a surprising social movement". We walk along a country road in order to see three of the wind turbines. They tower 77 meters above us in the flat countryside, a little taller than a Boeing 747 standing on end. They are ten years old 1 megawatt wind turbines, and will soon be outdated. Every turbine produces approximately 2533 MW per year and covers the annual con-

sumption of electricity in 630 homes. Interestingly, the three wind turbines in front of us are not owned by an energy company or by the state. The first one belongs to the farmer, on whose soil the turbine is erected. The second is a co-op wind turbine. And the last turbine? It belongs to Samsø's local landed gentry. Actually, wind turbines are not a new phenomenon on Samsø. Even today one can visit Denmark's would-be oldest existing windturbine, the post mill on Dansebjerg near Brundby. It was built on the island of Endelave in the beginning of the 16th century. In 1683 it was demolished and shipped to Samsø, where it was reconstructed.

The ten year effort has also resulted in the development of four heating stations, which supply heat to the villages on Samsø. One station consists of a heating system with solar panels and a wood chip burner, and the remaining three are straw-fired stations – obvious solutions on an island where farming is the main source of income. Two of the heating stations are run commercially by an energy company, one of them is a co-op venture, and the last one is owned by the consumers. More than 1000 houses are located in the countryside far from the large stations. For this reason they need their own heating stations. Almost 25% of them have replaced or supplemented the traditional oil-fired burners with solar heat, heat pumps or burners that run on biomass – wood chips, wood pellets, or straw.

Regardless of how you measure this development, Samsø is probably the world's most elaborate and multi-facetted example of how one can implement renewable energy in practice. Moreover, the experiment has unfolded in a society with one of the world's highest standards of living. Søren Hermansen thinks that the experiment on Samsø is a success, because it takes place on an island. It is a small and geographically defined community, where people know each other and have had to co-operate in order to survive. However, there is also a shadow side to the idyll. The rogue factor in Søren Hermansen's vision is Samsø's position on the map, which means that transport to the mainland will always be an issue. Even though a farmer has redesigned his car and tractor to run on rapeseed oil, the

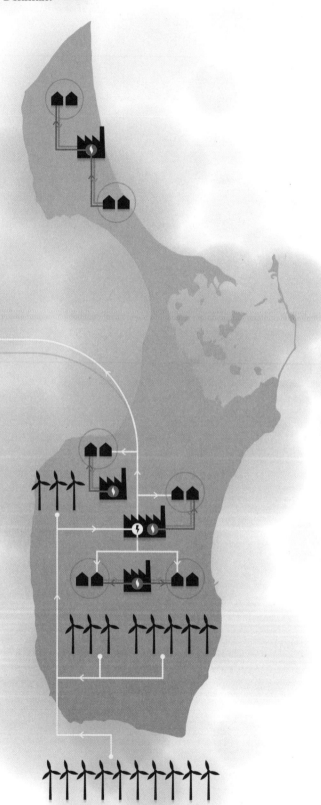

FROM 0 TO 100% IN TEN YEARS
—

Samsø's renewable energy project began in 1997. In those days, all heat and electricity came from fossil fuels. Ten years later, Samsø was 100% self-sufficient, producing electricity from renewable energy. The offshore wind turbines compensate for the entire transport related energy consumption.

The development means that Samsø today can showcase:

■ Eleven land based wind turbines that cover more than the island's electricity consumption

■ Ten offshore wind turbines – back-up and export to the mainland

■ Four district heating stations based on renewable energy sources – three straw-fired burners and one based on solar energy and wood chip combustion

■ Approximately 300 private homes that were not on the district heating stations have changed to renewable energy or supplement their fossil fuels with renewable energy – such as solar panels, pellet burners, and heat pumps.
—

ferries to and from the island, the cars, and the farming equipment still run on petrol and diesel. Nevertheless, Samsø still feels that it is 100 % self-sufficient in energy, because the 10 offshore wind turbines export more clean electricity to the mainland than the island uses on transport. On the green accounts, the clean electricity evens out the capacity of the fossil fuels. Of course Søren Hermansen has an electric car. It is a nine year old Citroën Saxo, which runs 50-60 kilometers on each recharge. That is not far, but it is OK for a small island. However, there are not many other electric cars on Samsø, They are simply too expensive.

"Like everyone else interested in electric cars we are waiting for cheaper prices and better technology. And again, I do not believe in a state-of-the-art project with electric cars that arrive pre-packed and ready, top-down from the mainland. Concepts that have already been formalized by energy companies, car manufacturers, and project managers are not always successful. People want to participate and they want to define how the cars should be used, how and when they should be recharged, what make of car they should have – and what the whole thing should cost. If you are only allowed to decide the color of your car – then I do not believe in it. Then you will be just another customer without responsibility, interest, and commitment, and there will be complaints and protests from day one. Innovation cannot be implemented top-down, it must come from below. Otherwise it just won't happen," says Søren Hermansen. And there are other challenges. If he looks ten years into the future, then he knows where to focus: ecology, farming, and waste.

THE DRIVING FORCE BEHIND GREEN INNOVATION ACCORDING TO SØREN HERMANSEN
—

■ By working down-up. There will be no changes without popular anchoring.

■ By demonstrating added value. What is in it for the individual citizen – any financial savings for example?
—

"Many tourists who come here are disappointed in our island and our renewable energy. They think that fruit, meat, and milk produced on Samsø are ecological. In fact, most of our produce is just traditional. However, at the moment I do not have great faith in ecology. The farming community makes too little money and is not ready for a change to ecological production. But who knows, perhaps in a couple of years..." Søren Hermansen has a practical approach, and ecology will have to wait till the conditions are more favorable. For this reason he is looking for new projects and waste and waste management are cardinal points.

"On Samsø we export our waste. We send it to Jutland, where it ends up in a district heating station. But waste has an inherent value. And we should not give it away," says the enthusiast from Samsø.

THE DANISH EXAMPLE

—

Even in Denmark, the world's leading country in the field of sustainable energy, the results of the experiments on the island of Samsø are remarkable. The island in the centre of the world's oldest kingdom has succeeded in doing what the Danish nation intends to accomplish by 2050: becoming independent of fossil fuels. Denmark has embarked on a quest and the Danish example is particularly interesting as a socioeconomic cost benefit case. Since 1980 Denmark has experience an economic growth of 78 percent, while the energy consumption and the CO_2 emission during the same period of time has declined. Today Denmark is one of the world's richest and most energy efficient countries. The tiny country has demonstrated that it is in fact possible to circumvent the connection between wealth and environmental strain.

Today renewable energy constitutes 19 percent of Denmark's total energy consumption. Contemplating this figure, one should bear in mind that the country does not have access to hydroelectric power. The windturbines have become the country's international brand, but also biomass, waste combustion, and decades of experimenting with efficient use of energy are central.

WEALTH AND REASON

—

"We cannot afford it." This is the most frequent argument against fighting climate change. In many ways it is a logical statement. It costs money to do research and develop new types of energy. We all know that electric cars are expensive and that electricity generated by windturbines is subsidized by the state. Still the argument is not correct. What we cannot afford is not to combat climate change. The American Secretary of energy

Steven Chu is an expert in energy. He is a Nobel Laureate in physics and he knows his arguments better than most people. Every day he meets Americans, many of them politicians, who say that America cannot afford to go green. Particularly in America, a high level of energy consumption is synonymous with economic activity, wealth, large cars and extravagant houses. Gorging on energy gives status.

In his characteristically understated way, Steven Chu disputes the contention that a high level of energy consumption equals wealth. In one of the PowerPoint slides he uses in his many speeches, he has merged two data streams – one describing the energy consumption of various countries and one outlining the same countries' position in the UN's global development index, the Human Development Index, which is a kind of ranking of the welfare of the individual countries. When cross referencing the two studies, the result is striking. It shows that the energy consumption is lowest in many of the countries which have the highest score on welfare – for instance Germany, Japan, and Holland.

One of Steven Chu's former colleagues, Daniel M. Kammen, who does research in alternative energy at UC Berkeley in California, uses a different line of reasoning. He poses a rhetorical question: Which two countries in the world have the highest energy efficiency performance? Denmark and Japan. Are they poor countries? No both countries are well-known for their wealth. They are also top of the OECD's energy efficiency index, which signifies that they have the best ability to squeeze GDP out of an energy unit. In an American context, he points to the state which by far has the strictest environmental laws and the highest energy efficiency: California. The sunny state reputedly has the most comprehensive economy in the USA, as well as an innovation dynamo which propels the American economy forward. Such low energy consumption can equal riches. But what about the monstrous expenses needed to fight climate change?

One of the world's most respected economists is the UK's Nicholas Stern, Lord Nicholas

THE ONLY GROWTH WE CAN AFFORD IS GREEN GROWTH.

Connie Hedegaard,
Climate and Energy Minister of Denmark
–

Stern, Baron of Brentford. In 2006 he published a groundbreaking study, commissioned by then Prime Minister Tony Blair, who had asked Stern to calculate the costs of combating climate change – and above all: what it would cost NOT to take on climate change. The results created newspaper headlines across the globe.

Stern and an entire team of top economists spent several years producing the report. The conclusion was that the price of fighting climate change will be around 1-2 percent of the GDP, the gross domestic product, per year. That is an astronomical figure, but the most interesting result of Stern's analyses was a different numeral: What does it cost NOT to do anything about the problem – what economists call "the cost of inaction". In short, what will it cost the world community to refrain from combating climate change and instead repair the damages by constructing dykes, protect cities against hurricanes, and treat people who are suffering from climate related diseases. It turned out to be much more expensive – and every year we postpone taking action, the price goes up. Stern predicted that if we do not stop the climate change in an efficient way right now, then the price in 2020

will escalate to figures between 5-20 percent of the GDP.

To sum up: Is it possible to simultaneously have a low energy consumption and be rich? Yes. Is it feasible to fight the climate change? Yes.

Stern's research is supported by other authoritative analyses carried out by among others the International Energy Agency, IPCC, and McKinsey & Co. Stern's conclusions opened up a new chapter in the discussion of "climate versus money" by pointing to the fact that the climate effort will not just be good business for a planet of joint ventures, but also a decisive driver in the development of a new phase of global growth.

The costs of the climate efforts are often at the centre of discussions. Stern and others began arguing in favor of considering the costs as investments – in new jobs, new industries, new research disciplines, new services and products. In other words what we consider economic growth. We could ask ourselves what would have happened, if Europe or Japan after WWII had decided that there were not enough funds in the coffers to rebuild what had been destroyed. Or if the Americans in the 1970s and the 1980s had taken a critical look at the enormous "costs" of developing fast micro processors, and then forgotten about it because it was too expensive.

In 2008 the Danish Energy Agency prepared a modest official memorandum which looks as tame as it is promising. "The Danish Example" sums up the facts, which have also been mentioned in this book: for thirty years Denmark has had a thundering economic growth without increasing the energy consumption or the CO_2 emission – while the proportion of renewable energy in 2009 reached a world record of 19 percent. At the same time the esteemed British magazine and rating agency *The Economist Intelligence Unit* has elected Denmark the most competitive country in the world. The memorandum is tucked away on the official COP15 homepage. However, it is most likely the most downloaded of all the files on the homepage. The Danish climate and energy minister Connie Hedegaard makes good use of it in the climate negotiations in order to counter the prejudices concerning a putative connection between the combat of climate change and economy.

One of the many interesting facts in the memorandum is that since 1995, the growth in the export of Danish products, related to the environment and energy, has been 400 percent. Today the sector accounts for 11 percent of Denmark's collective export.

A plethora of new research projects support the argument that a fight against climate change is an investment that will create growth. One of the more interesting research projects mentioned above was carried out by Daniel M. Kammen. It looks at the number of jobs created by the various types of energy production. The result is unequivocal: solar energy, wind energy, and energy efficiency create many more jobs than coal, oil, and gas. Up to eight times as many jobs.

In 2008 a black, underrated presidential candidate in the US used precisely these arguments in his election campaign. "In the next ten years we will invest 15 billion dollars every year in renewable energy, thereby creating five million new, green jobs which will pay off, which will not be outsourced, and which will help us become independent of foreign oil," said Obama during the final intense phase of the campaign. Today it sounds like a reliable

> ❝
> ## CHINA MAY LOOK LIKE A CO₂ GUZZLING MONSTER, BUT IN TERMS OF CLIMATE TECHNOLOGY, IT IS A SUPER POWER IN THE MAKING.
> ❞
>
> **Changhua Wu**,
> China Director, The Climate Group
> –

statement, but in 2008 the election pledge was a remarkable turning point in the perceived connection between the climate crisis and the economy. At the same time it was a turning point for the global environmental movement. The realization that the solution to environmental problems can be a solution to economic crises and that a presidential candidate in the world's number one capitalist super power wins by promoting this view, changed the public opinion.

Today the penny has dropped in most of the world. When the financial crisis struck in 2008/2009, governments around the globe voted for enormous growth packages, where part of the money would flow into the energy sector, into climate and jobs. However, the amounts were not nearly as large as those the climate experts had hoped for. Nevertheless, in the course of surprisingly few years, a gigantic shift of paradigm took place, as Adam Werbach of Saatchi & Saatchi S' points out.

The global laws which will effectively promote green innovation are of course still non-existent, but the EU, the Chinese, the Koreans, and the Indians are very determined to be the first to offer smart climate solutions – thereby creating wealth through climate protection.

If you are in doubt about whether or not the new realization has in fact made a difference, then you might just Google for fun the attitudes to the climate challenges that the world's three richest men – Bill Gates, Warren Buffet and Carlos Slim Helú – have. Yes, all three billionaires ardently advocate green growth. The latter, the Mexican telecommunications mogul, applies dry businessman's logic, when he replies: "Stabilizing and minimizing the emission of greenhouse gasses will demand important investments, which might not seem feasible – in the short perspective. However, in the long run the expenses will be much smaller than the costs, if climate change continue."

Another influential man is Hu Jintao, President of China, the leader of the world's greatest and most prospering economy. He has seen the opportunities, and in the words of Steve Howard from The Climate Group, he has unleashed a "climate dragon" in the realm of CO₂ friendly solutions. Today China is the country which erects the most windturbines. The Chinese are also at the cutting edge of solar energy, electric cars, and prestige projects like CO₂ neutral cities.

Illustration
Welfare versus energy consumption.
–
The graphics show that a high energy consumption does not equal welfare. Among countries that have the highest score in the UN's Human Development Index, you find countries with a relatively low electricity consumption.

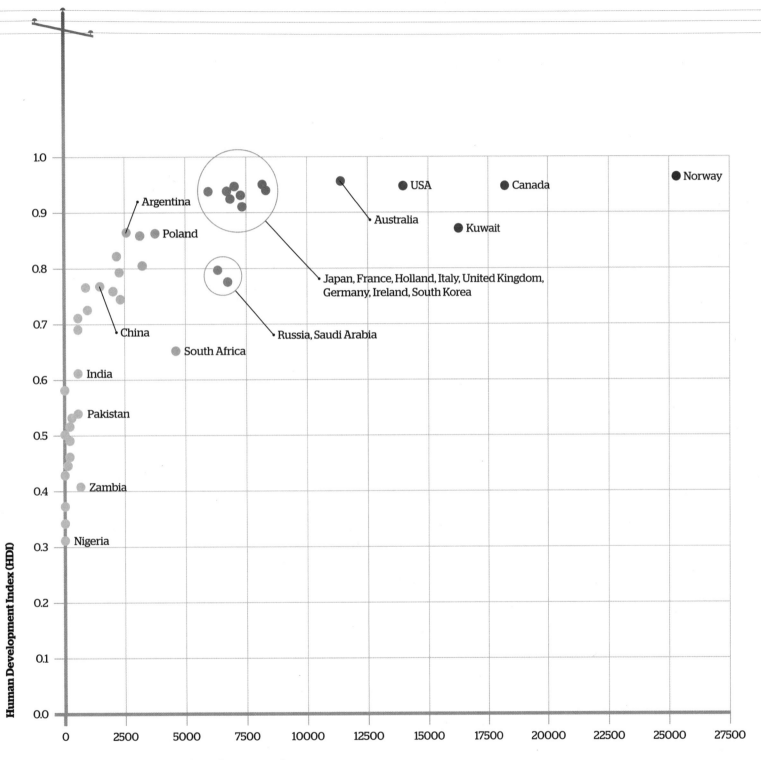

Human Development Index (HDI)

Electricity Consumption (kWh/person.year)

MILLIONS OF GREEN JOBS

—

In 2009 a research report commissioned by Tony Blair and The Climate Group showed that a new global climate agreement will result in ten million new green jobs worldwide. Another research project from The University of Berkeley in California shows how many jobs various types of energy generate per energy unit. It shows that the job potential in wind energy, solar energy, and energy efficiency is substantial - and greater than those found in traditional types of energy.

Illustration
The columns indicate that clean forms of energy like solar and wind create more jobs measured per produced energy unit, than for instance coal and natural gas. Energy efficiency also creates jobs.
Source: UC Berkeley.

Total job years per GWh

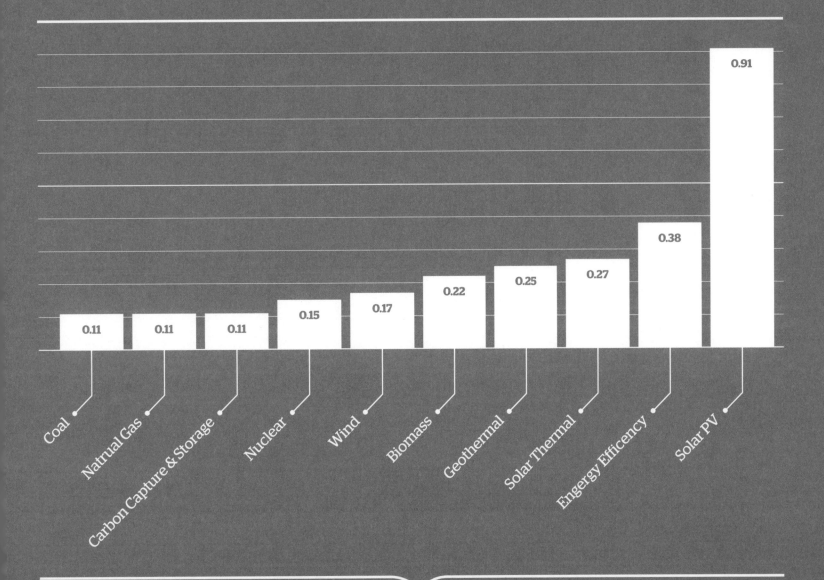

Technology

11/20
—
FROM HIGH TECH TO GREEN TECH

The Swedish entrepreneur Niklas Zennström is part of the legacy of the "last big thing" – the Internet revolution. In 2005, at the age of 39, he entered the IT Hall of Fame when the Internet giant eBay bought his online telephony network Skype, which he founded with his partner Janus Friis. Since then, he has given much attention to the next big thing, the green revolution, which the entrepreneur sees as a "huge change in markets" that will spur innovation and create opportunities for "making big bucks". And he knows what he is talking about. In 2005 the price tag on the very young company Skype was around 4 billion USD.

The journey from the high tech hey days of the 20th century to the green technologies of this century is one he has shared with many of his peers from Google, Microsoft, Am-

NIKLAS ZENNSTRÖM (1966)

—

Is co-founder of Zennström Philanthropies and currently a partner at Atomico, a venture capital firm. Niklas Zennström is an Internet entrepreneur who has co-founded several companies, including Joost, Skype, and Kazaa. Through Atomico he serves as a Board Member for several start-up companies. He holds dual degrees in Business and MSc Engineering Physics/Computer Science from Uppsala University in Sweden. He spent his final year at the University of Michigan, Ann Arbor and has won a series of industry awards including 'Innovation in Computing and Communications 2006' (*The Economist's Innovation Awards*) and the 'Wharton Infosys Business Transformation Award for Technology Change Agent of the Year 2006'. Niklas was also included in *Time Magazine*'s 100 Most Influential People List for 2006. Niklas Zennström is a Swedish citizen.

—

azon and Facebook. All of them have, in various ways, been attracted to the low carbon opportunities or supported environmental strategies. The innovative and technological component in both "revolutions" is obvious – and so are the rewards for those who first invent smart solutions. Not surprisingly, Google is a big investor in alternative energy, and Bill Gates spends part of his Microsoft fortune on philanthropy, including promotion of environmental protection.

Niklas Zennströmm does both investment and philanthropy – and he sees similarities and differences between high tech and green tech. "To some extent there are huge differences. In order to solve the climate change problem, we first need to have a robust regulatory framework – we then need innova-

tion and investments in those solutions. In the IT business we don't need that – we just need to solve a problem with innovation and marketing. Unfortunately, climate change is a much more difficult task. Having said that, I think that there are many similarities once we have a regulatory framework in place. I think we will see several innovative, disruptive products and low-carbon solutions, very similar to IT innovation and products.

"'The IT revolution' was really the second wave of IT evolvement. The most important elements were the expansion of the Internet, and the mobile phone networks, and the mainstreaming of the PC. The first two were chiefly accomplished by the established industry, the telecom industry. They were infrastructure building blocks that made it possible for an en-

tire field of innovations to flourish. Towards the end of the 1990s, we had the "dot.com boom and crash" – due to the fact that people were over-optimistic about moving any business online. But remember, we were still living in a dial-up world; the infrastructure was not really in place. With regards the present "green revolution": first of all, I think it's much too muted. What we really need is a flourishing of innovation and smart, cost-efficient low-carbon solutions as infrastructure – the equivalent of the Internet and mobile phone networks. The only difference is that the infrastructure in this case is mainly a robust regulatory framework and, ultimately, taxation of CO_2 emissions. Much of the venture capital that has gone into clean tech will encounter the same problem as some of the dot.com investments faced: they're

GOOD & GREEN

—

Zennström Philantropies has funded a series of scientific and policy oriented projects, but it is not just about giving away money. Zennström is a strong believer in collaborative approaches. One in which NGOs, investors, governments and individuals work together to achieve action and change.

Zennströmh Philanthropies has supported organizations like The Climate Group, Globe International and Environmental Defense Fund, seeking to inform and promote environmental policies, and donated significant amounts of money to initiatives that promote green entrepreneurship. An example is E+Co that makes clean energy investments in developing countries. With 15 years of experience and offices in 10 locations, E+Co's innovative business model provides lasting solutions to climate change and poverty. E+Co's business development support and investment capital serve to create energy businesses that have a positive social and environmental impact. Swedish Uppsala University has also received grants for a visiting professorship in climate change.

—

1.

1. The Swede Niklas Zennström (left) and the Dane Janus Friis founded the IT company Skype. In 2005 they sold it for approx. 4 billion dollars.

happening before the infrastructure is in place. I'm also certain that some will be very successful, just like Microsoft, Dell and Apple became successful in the early IT wave", he explains.

Zenströmm is a true entrepreneur himself and a serial founder of companies of which Skype is the most well known. The current list of start-ups in his portfolio is long (and yes, the brand names are innovative, too): Last.fm, Fon, Xobni, Technorati, Heysan and Woome. In 2007 he established The Zennström Philanthropies together with his wife, Catherine Zennström, and Salvatore

LaSpada. They focus on human rights and climate change, often with an emphasis on innovation. The thought-provoking quotes on the website are accordingly by both Buddhist leader Daisaku Ikeda and Californian governor Arnold Schwarzenegger ("This is our duty to those who share the world with us and to those who follow us: Wherever we see a threat to our environment, we must take action").

"To my mind, entrepreneurship and innovation are the things that, in my opinion, will become huge drivers behind a low-carbon economy" says Zennström. "As an entrepre-

> **I AM TRYING TO SPOT ANY MARKET DISRUPTION ON THE HORIZON THAT'S MORE SIGNIFICANT THAN THE TRANSFORMATION IN THE ENERGY SECTOR**

THE DRIVING FORCE BEHIND GREEN INNOVATION ACCORDING TO NIKLAS ZENNSTRÖM

—

Taxing carbon emissions would be the the single most effective way to promote green solutions. If this was suddenly done, it would make heaps of sense to invest in solar power, wind power, electric transportation, LED lights, etc. Entrepreneurs and innovators should not try to promote a specific technology, since it's very difficult for politicians to make decisions on that type of issue.

—

neur and venture capitalist, I always look for huge changes in the market – that's when you can make it big. When the status quo of the market changes because of a new technology (e.g. the Model T Ford, the steam engine, the Internet) or de-regulation (e.g. the 1998 European telecom deregulation, TV monopoly breakups, etc) the incumbent industry players are faced with something they don't usually like: they have to change in order to stay competitive. In most cases, this is very difficult – you have to inform your shareholders that you must lower your prices significantly, that you have to cannibalize your existing product line, or that it is necessary to let a large portion of your work force go. There are very few CEOs in public companies who have the leadership to do that. It's easier to pursue quarter's results instead. This opens up the field to the innovative and agile entrepreneur, who understands that when there's a problem, there's also a solution. I am trying to spot any market disruption on the horizon that's more significant than the disruption in the energy sector. The CO_2 curve is distressing because we're moving towards the worst case scenario according to the IPCC. This curve will have to decline in a substantial way, and when it does there will be huge opportunities for green entrepreneurs and green investors. Some of the more visionary incumbent industry players are trying to invest in low-carbon products, but they still defend their current polluting product lines".

Like other innovators of his generation – e.g. Uday Khemka from India – Zennström was influenced by one person: Former US vice president Al Gore: "The person who set off the alarm for me was Al Gore – in January 2005, I had the privilege of seeing him present his well-known slide show on climate change. It was not until then that I realized that climate change is the greatest and most imminent global threat to our planet. The presentation shocked me, and I realized that what I was doing - at that point in time I was very busy making Skype a successful company - was not very important compared to the threat our planet was facing. I subsequently began to work out plans as to how I could become philanthropically involved in the fight against climate change", Niklas Zennström tells, remembering his childhood: "Ever since I was a kid growing up in Sweden, I've always cared about nature and the environment – I guess I inherited those values from my parents. Over the years I have become increasingly concerned about our environment over the years. Specifically, I've been able to witness the changes to the Baltic Sea – my family has had a summer house there from the time I was born and I've always enjoyed sailing there. The changes to the Baltic that I've experienced have really upset me."

OBSTACL
CRUS
EVERY OBST
TO STERN
HE WHO IS FI
DOES NOT CH

Leonardo Da Vinci:
Notebooks

CANNOT
ME.

CLE YIELDS

RESOLVE.

ED TO A STAR

NGE HIS MIND.

12/20

—

THE ALCHE-MIST

There is a good reason why Indians have always called the constituent state Kerala for God's own country. The green state is located at the south western end of the Indian subcontinent with the Arabian Sea in its backyard and with an address as close to paradise on earth as you can get. The sun always shines and the temperatures are around 30 degrees all year round. The coconut palms stand shoulder to shoulder throughout most of the country and the food is exquisite. However, the leftovers and the waste from the good meals are everywhere apparent. Piles of banana peels are left to rot in the gutter, fish heads, vegetable tops and broken coconuts accumulate along with plastic, paper and dirt. Many families attempt to get a grip on the accumulation of waste by burning it in the backyard. Compared to

SAJI DAS (1965)

–

Born and raised in Thiruvananthapuram. He has a master's degree in sociology, and began to work on biogas projects already in his student days. In 1994, he founded Biotech NGO in order to increase the knowledge about and the use of biogas. He also founded two companies that manufacture the elements for the biogas plants. He has received numerous recognitions for his work, among others the Ashden Awards 2007 (picture).

–

Indian standards, the standard of living is relatively high in Kerala and rising. The amount of waste increases hand in hand with the welfare of the nation – but only half of the waste in the popular tourist state is collected.

For years, waste has been accumulating. However, a young student of sociology, Saji Das, saw a glimmer of gold in the rotting fish scales. Initially, he was just abhorred and disgusted by the enormous, smelly mountains of waste in the streets and alleyways of the city. But then Saji Das began to think. What if the waste could be used? What if one could turn a problem into a useful advantage?

Today, Saji Das runs a unique business which lives up to the relatively new and yet well-established principle of benefitting the triple bottom line "people, planet, and profit" – a principle which not only shows consideration for the economy, but also for the social and environmental income. Saji Das has invented a process that benefits thousands of poor Indians every day. At the same time, it not only removes waste from the streets, it also reduces the CO_2 emission from households all over India. And mind you, his invention comes at a price which is affordable to any ordinary Indian family.

Like most good ideas, his invention is extremely simple: Saji Das has produced a biogas plant that can be installed in any home. The organic waste goes into the plant, which then produces biogas for the stove. The remains of the process can be used as fertilizer in the garden. In a country with more than one billion inhabitants, the perspective is tremendous. Of course Saji Das has even greater plans.

The 45-year-old Das trained as a sociologist. He himself thinks that the road from sociology to green technology is logical.

"I began studying sociology because I was interested in my society and in the living conditions of poor people. That interest has not changed," says Saji Das.

We are sitting in his office at Biotech in the centre of Thiruvananthapuram, the capital of Kerala.

The walls reflect the recognition and credits with which the Indian biogas pioneer has been inundated at home and abroad. The

PLANTS
—

A Biotech plant consists of two air-tight containers, placed one above the other. The first is a concrete organic waste container – often partly sub-merged in the backyard. The second is a tank for the accumulation of gas. Bacteria degrade and transform the kitchen refuse to methane gas. Via a hose the gas is transferred directly to a custom built gas stove in the kitchen.

A typical domestic plant can proc-ess five kilos of organic waste and 20 liters of fluid every 24 hours. The plant runs on peelings from fruit and vegetables, fish heads, meat scraps, etc. The kitchen refuse is gathered in a bucket and mixed with water – e.g. dirty cleaning water – and poured directly into the plant. The plant does not smell.

Some of the large plants designed for schools and institutions can also process waste from toilets.
—

> **WE ALL PRODUCE KITCHEN REFUSE ON A DAILY BASIS. IT IS FULL OF ENERGY, AND IF THE GARBAGE IS TRANSFORMED TO BIOGAS, THE INDIVIDUAL HOUSEHOLD CAN CONTRIBUTE TO ITS OWN ENERGY SUPPLY.**

wall is full of certificates, figurines, plaques and marks of distinction. There are photos of Saji Das with the British Crown Prince Charles and there is one where the shy Indian entrepreneur, properly attired in a suit and a striped silk tie, shakes hands with the world's no. 1 environmentalist Al Gore.

Interrupted by constantly ringing phones, Saji Das explains how studying sociology became a springboard to a career as a frontrunner in the field of biogas. As a student he was looking for a part time job. "As I was interested in the environment and in energy supply, I signed up for a course in biogas. I also figured that later there might a job in this field for me," says Saji Das.

He was right - even though it took a couple of years before he became fully aware of the connection between waste and energy.

In 1994, he founded Biotech NGO and during the first year he was the manager as well as the only employee. The following year, he hired his first co-worker and today, years later, he is the richer for experience, experiments, and biogas plants. Now Biotech employs 70 people on a permanent basis and 250 skilled laborers and counselors on a freelance basis.

Saji Das' basic approach was to distribute biogas plants in the larger cities. In the first four years, he constructed several hundred small and less successful biogas plants. The four years of practical experience made it possible for him to manufacture a plant prototype, which with a spray of dirty water or fluid transformed the family's paper bags, chili stems, fish tails, and rotten pineapple to biogas. A small household plant can reduce a family's consumption of bottled gas or petroleum with 50%.

Saji Das quickly understood that there was a huge potential in the marketplace for his plant.

"We all produce kitchen refuse on a daily basis. It is full of energy, and if the garbage is transformed to biogas, the individual household can contribute to its own energy supply," he says.

"This realization was for me a significant turning point. Since then I have dedicated my time exclusively to the propagation of the technology, the development of new models, and to the education of people who can install the plants and give advice on the operation and the maintenance of the plant," says Saji Das.

Today there are larger and more efficient systems designed for schools, hospitals and

FROM IDEA TO REALITY
—
The prototype for the first plant in the production of biogas from foodwaste was ready in 1998. Since then nine models of different sizes have been developed.
■ There are 16,000 operative plants in private households.
■ There are 200 operative plants in schools, hospitals, and other institutions.
■ There are 40 large integrated operative plants for the processing of waste in municipalities, markets, slaughterhouses, etc.
—

other public institutions, slaughterhouses, fish markets, etc.

A typical household can process five kilos of waste every 24 hours, while a large system is capable of processing one ton of waste in this time. One ton of organic waste supplies energy to 500 street lamps. Several of the large biogas systems also digest waste from the latrines of schools and institutions. Most of the systems operate locally in Kerala, but by and by they can be found all over India. Furthermore, the export is increasing. Licensed production of the digesters is happening in a number of countries in Africa and the rest of Asia.

Basically, a digester system consists of a tank, where bacteria transform food waste and other biological material. The entire process is started by adding e.g. cow manure, when the plant is used for the first time. When the plant

**" CONCERNING THE PRODUCTION OF
BIOGAS, I THINK WE ARE ABOUT TO SEE A
MAJOR BREAKTHROUGH IN THE
APPLICATION OF KITCHEN REFUSE AND
OTHER WASTE PRODUCTS. BOTH THE
SUPPLY AND THE DEMAND ARE
GROWING RAPIDLY. "**

is operative, the family throws kitchen waste into the plant on a daily basis along with the dirty household water. A fluid element is important. Water, blood from the slaughterhouse, or waste from the latrine must be added. In the course of the decomposition process, biogas is released in the form of methane. The gas is collected in a separate tank, where it is stored for cooking purposes. When the biogas is distributed from the tank, a fine and clean surplus product remains. It contains a lot of nutrients and can be used as fertilizer in the garden. In private households, the tanks are often buried halfway into the ground in the back garden or positioned just outside the kitchen window.

An ordinary Indian household can extract enough biogas to keep the pots simmering for about two hours every day. The biogas thus replaces half or more of the bottled gas or the petroleum, which is normally used for cooking. The cheapest plant costs 10,000 rupees – little more than 200 dollars. Considering the money saved on energy, an investment

in a plant has paid itself off in around three years. Biogas plants also contribute to the reduction of CO_2 in the atmosphere – partly because of the direct replacement of fossil fuels, partly because less fuel must be transported to the country and the home. The source of energy is just outside the kitchen window.

Even though the advantages of transforming kitchen waste to biogas are obvious, many kilos of waste are still burnt every day in thousands of backyards in Kerala. The main reason is that many families quite simply cannot afford a plant.

The Indian authorities subsidize part of the expenses to the extent that a buyer can get a refund of around 50% of the price. However, only every other applicant is granted support for the purchase of a biogas plant.

"At the moment, the price and the lack of public subsidies constitute the largest hurdle in the proliferation of the technology. Nevertheless, I believe that we are facing an ever greater breakthrough in the application

of biogas and the transformation of kitchen waste and other waste. We feel that there is a significant increase in the demands as well as the supplies," Saji Das points out.

He and his co-workers do their best to spread the knowledge about biogas plants. They give talks and teach school children, go out and demonstrate the plants on the street and in the marketplaces, they attend conferences and write articles for newspapers and magazines. Saji Das still develops new models of the biogas plant. He is also in charge of the company's research and development. Recently, he has initiated a co-operation with the Swiss Federal Institute of Environmental Service and Technology. Furthermore, he travels extensively in order to give talks about the advantages in the transformation of food waste to biogas. "I am incredibly grateful for everything we have achieved so far. However, as I have already said, I believe the momentum will increase and become much more significant," Saji Das emphasizes.

13/20
—
SMOKE

It sounds too good to be true. And the man behind the idea admits as much. It's what comes from "creating something that nobody has ever heard of, or even thought of, something that was just science fiction." Chew Hwee Hong, the founder and managing director of Ecospec, exudes passion, engaging the world with the ardor of a born proselytizer, one possessing an important but little-known secret. Chew's secret? His Singapore-based firm might have cracked one of the defining challenges of this century: finding a way to extract carbon dioxide –CO_2 - from smokestacks.

In 2008, Chew was approached by Tardic Tonci, an engineer at Tanker Pacific, with a challenge. Tonci asked if Ecospec, which had long experience in treating wastewater without chemicals, could come up with a solu-

CHEW HWEE HONG

—

Founder and Managing Director, Ecospec, is a marine engineer by training. He says all his training and experience went into the development of CSNOx, including marine engineering, cathodic protection corrosion control, physics, chemistry, water treatment, microorganism controls, and even the knowledge gained from his personal hobbies of mineral specimen collecting, gemology, and marine biology. In 2001, he founded Ecospec with the objective to provide a good solution for the non-chemical treatment of wastewater. This knowledge was then put to use to produce a series of products that provided the basis for the development of CSNOx.

—

"...IT IS ESSENTIAL THAT CSNOX BE INTRODUCED IN A BUSINESS WAY, MAKING IT EASIER AND PRACTICAL FOR ALL TO IMPLEMENT EFFECTIVELY TO SAVE THIS WORLD, OTHERWISE IT WILL JUST BE ANOTHER USELESS AND BURIED GOOD IDEA OR GOOD INNOVATION."

tion for removing CO_2 from his ships' smokestacks. Chew and a team of researchers, including chairman Foo Onn Fah, set to work. Chew, a marine engineer by training, says that "everything I had learned in my life was put to use" in the solution Ecospec developed in late 2008 and introduced to the world in January 2009, a technique called CSNOx. The acronym captures the elegant simplicity of the technology, an all-in-one solution that removes CO_2, sulfur dioxide - SO2 -, nitrogen oxides –Nox-, and soot from exhaust flue gas.

Existing methods to remove these gases, as well as particulates, from the smokestacks of merchant ships target the pollutants individually, often using chemicals in energy-intensive processes that can generate additional CO_2 emissions.

Upwards of 100,000 ships ply the seas ferrying goods around the globe; the fuel burned by these ships account for 4.5 % of global greenhouse gas emissions. Based on these numbers alone, and accounting for the emissions-cutting potential of CSNOx, the implications for the fight against climate change are clear. But Chew's vision does not stop with global shipping. It encompasses power plants and refineries and waste incinerators and factories, the onshore facilities responsible for most of mankind's emissions.

Ecospec is well on its way to commercializing CSNOx in the maritime industry. The technology has the backing of the American Bureau of Shipping, and soon will be tested by the International Maritime Organization. Nearly a dozen ship projects are under way. Even so, Chew knows the real potential of CSNOx is onshore. Here, Ecospec is working on both open- and closed-loop systems: open for facilities close to a water source, such a power plant sited along a river, where treated water could be released back to the source; closed for power plants in remote regions where freshwater or groundwater is scarce and must be recycled. Chew says that the company is currently designing a closed-loop system for an incinerator project. By the end of 2009, Ecospec hopes to start a refinery project in Singapore.

Despite the promise of CSNOx, Chew readily acknowledges that the technology was received with the skepticism all too familiar to inventors trying to convince the world they've designed the next big thing. After a prototype of the CSNOx system was tested on an oil tanker in December 2008, and results announced in January 2009, for instance, the government of Singapore wanted to know, says Chew, *Is this for real?* In response, Ecospec built an onshore test rig outfitted with CSNOx to give Singaporean officials and investors the opportunity to watch the system in action and test and verify the results.

SCRUBBING

—

CSNOx removes carbon dioxide (CO_2), sulfur dioxide (SO_2), nitrogen oxides (NOx), and soot from the exhaust flue gas of smokestacks, without chemicals, by increasing the alkalinity of seawater. Seawater is fed into an Ultra-Low Frequency System that boosts its pH level from the normal 8.1 to 10. The highly alkaline water is then sprayed directly into the exhaust flue chamber, where it reacts with and absorbs pollutants, neutralizing them into harmless sulfates, nitrates, and carbonates that are beneficial to marine life. After scrubbing, solid particles are removed, and the recovered water, with further treatment, can either be discharged, or, in arid areas, recycled back to the scrubbing process. According to Ecospec, tests show that CSNOx removes up to 93% of SO_2, 82% of NOx, and nearly 75% of CO_2.

—

"I've started many new businesses, in many different fields, and am used to failures, obstacles," says Chew. "However, the CSNOx development is one that gave the most challenges. The most important part is the, 'never say die,' strong fighting spirit. It must be there all times to overcome all the problems." Asked about the obstacles overcome, Chew credits the wisdom that only comes with living – that and a good dose of luck. "As you get older, you become wiser and you began to realize many things happened in life are beyond our own control. I never expected we could roll out a product or invention that is first-in-the-world and could possible extend the life of this planet. There were so many incredible findings in the course of our CSNOx work that just happened in front of us and were given to

99

CSNOX IS HERE TO EXTEND THE LIFE OF THIS PLANET. AS LONG AS IT IS SUCCESSFULLY IMPLEMENTED ACROSS THE WORLD, MY JOB IS DONE IN THIS LIFE.

99

us. It is being arranged to have CSNOx come to this world – and not because we are smart or clever. We're just the human beings arranged to execute the work, that's all."

But, if Chew is right, even if the world seems to *want* CSNOx to succeed, in the end, it still has to make business sense. A point not lost on Chew. "There are many easier ways to make money than CSNOx. For Ecospec shareholders, although making money is critical to keep the company going, it is certainly not the prime mover. For CSNOx to be successfully implemented across the world, it is essential that CSNOx be introduced in a business way, making it easier and practical for all to implement effectively to save this world, otherwise it will just be another useless and buried good idea or good innovation."

Talking with Chew Hwee Hong, you quickly realize that he is a man keenly aware both of the gravity of the threat posed to humanity by climate change and that time is running out to do something about it. He has dedicated his personal wealth and career to telling the world about CSNOx. "Personally, I prefer a low-profile, simple life. But for CSNOx marketing and PR purposes, there is no choice but to act as a front man to make CSNOx known to the world. And all the millions made in the past were happily drained into the CSNOx. But life is more meaningful than before," says Chew.

To Chew, the fate of the planet and the success of Ecospec and CSNOx are very much intermingled. He sees his role in the climate change fight to be convincing the owners of every ship, power plant, refinery, incinerator,

cement plant, or pulp-and-paper mill – the facilities that power and supply the economic churn of our ever-demanding world – to install his technology. "My personal stake is to produce, and make the world accept, CSNOX. The CSNOx invention is an excellent weapon to fight against human-induced climate change, but how well this good weapon can be used by the world will be in the hand of destiny. My part is to introduce the CSNOx name to the world. Every new CSNOx system installed, it is a step forward for all of us!" He adds, "CSNOx is here to extend the life of this planet. As long as it is successfully implemented across the world, my job is done in this life."

14/20
–
ENERGY OF THE GIANTS

This is whale country. In the shallow waters near Breakwater and Cape Cod not far from Boston, and in the depths along the Atlantic coastline near Nantucket and Martha's Vineyard you find one of the world's largest whale populations. Humpback whales, right whales, and even the extremely rare blue whale, the world's largest mammal. It was from this location that Captain Ahab set out to sea in his tireless pursuit of the white whale Moby Dick in Herman Melville's famous novel. I meet Curtis Felix on the Boston waterfront, where the whaling ships lie side by side. For centuries this part of the ocean has been a larder for the giants of the sea, and every year during summer they gather here in order to feast on the ample supply of plankton, small crayfish, spawn, and bacteria. Curtis Felix is

not a whaler, but he has his own "white whale",
an objective he wishes to realize: He wants to
make it possible for mankind to make use of
the whales' source of energy. Plankton.

Curtis Felix's company is called Plankton
Power, and it is based in Massachussets and
in Chubut in Argentina. Along the Argentin-
ian coastline the ocean is saturated with tiny
nourishing algae, which attract whales in
great numbers. Plankton Power intends to
produce and refine biodiesel in closed circuit
tank farms on the basis of micro-algae . They
utilize solar cell technology to power the lights
suspended above the algae, thereby speeding
up the natural development of biological oil. A
refinery transforms the oil to biodiesel, which
then can be pumped directly into the existing infrastructure and used in cars, airplanes,
and heating systems in houses. "For the next
decades we need to produce fluid, clean fuel,
which can be distributed by the present filling
stations and pipelines. It would be extremely
costly to build a new infrastructure," Curtis
Felix explains, who has dedicated his life to
the project.

Felix has worked in the North and South
American energy industries for more than
thirty years. However, during all these years
his focus has been on energy efficiency and alternative sources of energy. Since 2007, he has
put everything he owns into Plankton Power, a
classic example of a promising green technology on the verge of a commercial breakthrough. It is all lined up: The first demonstration project has been carried out in Argentina
and the result was impressive: an annual
production of 3,8 million liters of bioenergy.
More customers are ready and waiting, among
them the Massachussetts National Guard,
which has also agreed to supply the land

" WE USE POISONOUS FUEL AND WE DON'T CONSIDER THE CONSEQUENCES. "

on which the first pilot algae farm, complete with production plant and refinery, will be constructed., Curtis has established a team of scientists consisting of thirty of the world's leading experts on algae from the local Woods Hole Oceanographic Institution and Marine Biological Laboratory, and they receive great support from the local authorities and politicians. Plankton Power is expected to generate hundreds of green jobs in Massachussets.

The secret behind algae plankton is that it contains very large amounts of oil, in fact 20 times more than palm oil and 300 times more than soy oil – and that plankton blooms extremely fast. In a matter of three weeks, the recently formed organism will mature – and one can "harvest" the energy. That means that compared with biomass cultivated on land, such as corn, algae produce 50-100 times more energy per hectare. "Our great breakthrough occurred when we found out how to combine solar cells and bioenergy. A production based on this combination consumes much less energy. The fact that we work with cold water plankton, as opposed to others who work with warm water plankton, contributes to the energy ratio. Actually I believe it is quite banal:

CURTIS FELIX (1960)
–
Graduated in economy and political science. He worked in the energy sector for 30 years, in among other capacities as energy economist in the World Bank and in various utility companies. In the 1990s he founded his first alternative energy company Alternative Vehicle Service Group. It established the natural gas based traffic system which to this day drives busses and vehicles in Boston's Logan airport. In 2009 Plankton Power was appointed one of the world's 50 most promising bioenergy companies.
–

Everone thinks that algae bloom faster in hot water, but that is actually not the case. Cold water plankton is just as efficient – and you do not have to heat up the water," says Curtis Felix.

The environmental advantage is that plankton energy is not made out of sources that would otherwise be consumed as food

– such as sugar cane, corn, or palm oil, which would involve the felling of trees in tropical zones. The technique has already been developed, as opposed to the so-called second generation bioenergy, developed on the basis of for instance waste. Furthermore, plankton farms kan be placed almost anywhere, they need not take up valuable land, and they do not require fertilizer or pesticiedes. "I once worked in Brazil and spent a lot of time in the rain forest. I looked at the local trees and plants which grow at amazing speed and I thought: That is fantastic. Think of all that energy. Benjamin Franklin must have experienced this feeling, when he saw a lightning. [Franklin was the first scientist who proved that a lightning is an electrical discharge]. Wow, what a lot of energy! It should be possible to tap that energy for a useful purpose!" Curtis Felix laughs.

And the potential is substantial. By using the equivalent of two percent of America's agricultural land for plankton farms, biodiesel made out of algae will be able to cover the entire transport energy consumption of the USA. Is the market interested in sustainable fuels? Yes, airlines such as Virgin and Continental are deeply committed to making

1.

PLANKTON POWER TO THE PEOPLE
—

Plankton Power produces biodiesel from oil extracted from micro-algae. Plankton consists of the enormous amounts of organisms floating in the ocean – 10-20 million organisms per liter water. Plankton consists of animal plankton as well as plant plankton such as algae. The cultivation process takes place in closed tanks, so-called photobioreactors, where plankton is exposed to controlled amounts of light. The technology applied is the same as that which you find in solar panels. The oil is extracted and subjected to a refining process, which results in biodiesel that can be used just like ordinary diesel in for instance cars, airplanes, and heating.
—

2a.

2b.

experiments in biobased fuels, which can solve their CO_2 problem.

Until mid 2009 the future looked bright for Power Plankton. A private venture fund had decided to invest 20 million dollars in the project. Then the financial crisis arrived, the fond had to pull out, and it has turned out to be almost impossible to raise alternative private capital. Today, Power Plankton is waiting for a response to an application for a similar amount from Barack Obama's new subsidies for green technology. Without a subsidy it will be just as difficult for Felix to realize his dream, as it was for Captain Ahab to find the white whale in Melville's famous novel. On the whole, Curtis Felix does not understand why

the USA is so unambitious when it comes to green technology. "If we introduced a quota system for CO_2, it would necessarily inspire innovation that would give us an edge. Regardless of the circumstances, the market for clean technology will be here to stay. The Chinese and the Indians want to buy the technology. Right now they are in the same position as we were in the beginning of the twentieth century. The air in their cities is so polluted that the citizens demand action and cleaner technology. Just think of the Olympic Games in Beijing. When the citizens of Beijing for a short period of time experienced what it is like to breathe clean air, they naturally demanded clean air on a daily basis. So it is all about putting

yourself in an advantageous position first. The person who develops the technology wins. These are the technologies of the future. It is like inventing the computer. If you can invent a cheap, high-performance computer, then you win," says Felix, who thinks that security in the areas of supply and pricing plays an even greater role than global warming. Instead of buying oil at prices artificially inflated by dictatorships, it is in every country's interest to develop energy sources which are not just

1. Energy from the ocean. Scenic view of the island Martha's Vineyard on the Massachusetts coastline.

2a-b. Plankton grown in closed system tanks.

**THE DRIVING FORCE BEHIND
GREEN INNOVATION ACCORDING TO
CURTIS FELIX**

—

■ "Energy pricing that reflects the
real costs – including environmental
and health costs."
■ "Create a long-term political framework, that provides security for the
investors."

—

located in certain geographical areas. Micro-
algae are more or less a global phenomenon,
he says and points out that the climates in
Norway, Sweden, and Denmark are perfect for
the same type of algae as those farmed in the
tanks at Plankton Power.

What is the best thing the politicians
can do for Felix? He is not in doubt: Pollution
should be priced. "For thirty years we have
known that the price of petrol does not reflect
the actual expenses. The costs related to acid
rain, climate change, and increased cancer
risk is not part of the calculation. We use poisonous fuel and we don't stop to consider the
consequences," he concludes with a frustrated
shrug. When there is a crisis, the uneven price
competition does not encourage investments
in projects like Plankton Power. Curtis Felix
makes no bones about the fact that the application for government funding is the final call
for Plankton Power. If it is not honored, he has
two choices: To mortgage his house in order
to be able to continue just a little longer or to
definitively give up using the giant whales'
source of energy which is floating in the sea
water just outside the windows.

DRIVING
ON
SUGAR

—

While the rest of the world is discussing biopetrol, the entire car fleet of Brazil is running on alternative fuels – mostly bioethanol produced from sugar cane. More than 40 years ago the Brazilians gradually began mixing petrol with ethanol from the sugar cane industry. Today it is legally established that Brazilian private cars must mix at least 26 percent bioethanol into the petrol, and all cars have the option to run on several types of fuel. Many are running on clean ethanol. It costs half as much as petrol.

TWENTY
SOLUTIONS TO THE CLIMATE CRISIS

—

These are the technologies, which can prevent dangerous climate change. Each of them promotes a pronounced reduction of the CO_2 emission. Combined, they will be able to lower the world's CO_2 emission sufficiently, but only if we develop and share them efficiently and quickly. According to the economists, the available "green" technologies to the right will be cost-free or profitable, if you write them off over a period of many years. It would for instance make good business sense for society to insulate buildings efficiently, thereby saving energy. The red technologies to the right will need investments. All things considered, it will cost us 1-3 percent of the global GDP (Gross Domestic Product) to combat the climate change with these technologies.

Source: McKinsey & Co

Illustration
These twenty well-known technologies can solve our CO_2 problem - if we invest in them. In a longer perspective the green technologies yield a profit. The red technologies need additional investments.

Fuel Efficient cars and commercial vehicles

Building insulation

Lighting systems

Air-conditioning

Water heating

Sugarcane biofuel

Standby losses Nuclear

Livestock

CCS (Carbon Capture and Storage)

Forest protection

Industrial feedstock substitution

Industrial motor systems Windturbines

Co-firing biomass

low-cost forestation

Methane capture from rubbish dumps

Coal-to-gas-shift

Coal retrofit

Biodiesel

15/20
—
A DREAM TAKES FLIGHT

As a child Massimo Ippolito dreamt of driving plutonium-fuelled cars that floated through the streets. Today he dreams of getting hundreds, even thousands of lightweight kites airborne way up above the clouds, where they can transform strong winds to clean energy. While he has realized that cars floating on plutonium fuel are an idle dream, he has long since sent the first kites into the troposphere.

Throughout the last nine years the 51-year-old engineer Massimo Ippolito and his consolidated team have explored the function of kites in the Torino province in the north west of Italy. "Kite Generator" or "Kite Gen" is a large scale project that taps into the resources of strong winds about one kilometer above the surface of the earth. The kites are made of textile sails spanning around 1200 square

MASSIMO IPPOLITO (1958)

—

Is a graduate in engineering from the Politecnico in Torino. When he finished his studies, he worked for the company Polielettronica at Ferrara. In 2000 he founded the company Sequoia Automation, where he still holds a position on the board. Among Ippolito's many other patents is the intelligent sensor SeTAC, which won the German "Industrie Preis 2008".

—

1. Massimo Ippolito insists on being photographed with his Kite Gen-team. Massimo Ippolito is no. 3 from the right.

1.

meters – about the size of the plot of a large single-family house. The kites are sent up into the strong perpetual winds of the troposphere. The large kites are constructed according to the template used by the kite surfers delighting in speed on the waters of the Lake Garda, the Californian beaches, and the coasts of Thailand. However, instead of being attached to a human being, Kite Gen's kites are connected to a generator – a carousel – on earth. When the kites circulate above the clouds, they activate the generators on the ground and produce energy.

Several years of calculations and outdoor experiments with smaller models and in Kite Gen's laboratory confirm that in theory the large kites can produce electricity at a price at least 30 times cheaper than the present European average price. What's more, the kites will be producing clean and sustainable energy. Kite Gen is in the process of building its first plant in the engineer's native village of Berzano di San Pietro, which has 400 inhabitants. The intention is that the plant should supply the village with electricity. At the moment the Kite Gen Company only needs to get permission from the Italian air traffic controllers. Then the kites will be airborne. The permission is expected to be ratified within a few months.

"Having worked as an engineer for twenty years in the fields of electronics, electrical systems, and automatics, I revised my thoughts and began thinking of an enormous resource – the high altitude winds above the clouds," says Massimo Ippolito. Massimo Ippolito has made many inventions and has patented a fair share of them. "Ideas," he says, "come to me at a rate of 20-30 an hour. But what am I supposed to do with them? What counts is turning them into reality."

The highflying idea of sending kites into the troposphere is well on its way to be put into practice. The actual basis of Kite Gen is one of Massimo Ippolito's many patents. In fact

it is a small, so-called intelligent sensor weighing only 54 grams. It is capable of steering, controlling and anticipating the movements of the giant sails that have brought the high altitude wind project to the world's attention. One thing is to get the kite airborne – another is to control and utilize its movements. The prize-winning SeTAC sensor is applied for example in industrial robots and as a replacement for the artificial horizon in smaller planes..

Massimo Ippolito's combined interest in technical issues, electronics, and the environment was stimulated from an early age. His father worked in the environmental section at Fiat and he coached his sons in questions of energy and stressed that a shortage of energy would be one of the greatest problems in the future. According to Massimo Ippolito, it is our habits of consumption that are leading us directly into the abyss. He proudly emphasizes that he has owned only one washing machine in his entire adult life. As expected, he also reveals that his home is packed with things that need to be repaired.

"I am worried about the development... Mankind has lost touch with reality. We have lost our roots in the farming community and today we are nothing more than consumers," he says. Ippolito's work commands great interest at home and abroad. On the shelf behind the great work table in the laboratory you will find among many other prizes, a recognition given to him by the Italian ministry of the environment for his new and creative thoughts. However, Massimo Ippolito's experiences with the political establishment are not all good. He is concerned about the lack of insight and interest displayed by ministers of the environment and other politicians. Actually the Italian engineer would much rather spend time at home with his wife or in his laboratory. The success of Kite Gen has engendered another dilemma: these days a lot of attention is directed towards Massimo Ippolito as a person.

—

Since the year 2000 the people behind Kite Gen have experimented with kites in order to generate energy in the troposphere several hundred meters above the surface of the Earth. Gigantic lightweight kites, reminiscent of those used for windsurfing are propelled 80–200 meters up into the air by ventilators. At this level the winds are lifted by the high altitude winds to a height of 800 meters – sometimes even as high as 1000–1500 meters, where the winds are both stronger and more constant. The figure eight movements of the kites that increase and decrease in altitude activate the generators on the ground in the Kite Gen centre. The initial experiments resulted in a great number of exploded balloons, before the invention of flexible "stalks" which secure the lines to the kites. The decisive breakthrough arrived when the kites were fitted with a sensor created by Massimo Ippolito. The sensor functions as an autopilot, which can steer the kites on short notice –if for instance a flock of birds approach the plant or if two kites in a future Kite Gen consisting of 10-20 kites are about to collide. According to the experiments, Kite Gen will be capable of accumulating energy for more than 5000 hours every year – twice as much as most up-to-date wind turbines. With limited plant expenses Kite Gen is capable of producing electricity at a price 30 times less than the present average price in Europe.

—

> ❞
> # I AM WORRIED ABOUT THE DEVELOPMENT... MANKIND HAS LOST TOUCH WITH REALITY. WE HAVE LOST OUR ROOTS IN THE FARMING COMMUNITY AND TODAY WE ARE NOTHING MORE THAN CONSUMERS.
> ❞

THE DRIVING FORCE BEHIND GREEN INNOVATION ACCORDING TO MASSIMO IPPOLITO
—
■ "I am a humanist and my dream is to install Kite Gens in countries, which cannot afford to do so themselves."
■ "We must apply energy in order to give everyone in the world equal opportunities. Either we all live well or the planet will become uninhabitable."
—

"I am a laboratory bear and my idea of a good life is to develop ideas with my team. However, in the last few years I have to a great extent lost my laboratory innocence."

The Italian kite flyer is not easy to label and he certainly does not want to be controlled either. This attitude has influenced Kite Gen in significant ways. When there is talk about venture capital, about transfer of rights and patents and sending Kite Gen to talk to lawyers employed by solvent companies, Ippolito shakes his head. For this reason several million dollars donated by Google went to a wind project in California instead of to the Torino province. "I am a humanist and I simply want everyone to benefit from Kite Gen," he says. "Caimans" – or "voracious crocodiles" – are his nicknames for all those who are waiting to grab patents and ideas with the single objective of making profit. Formally speaking, Kite Gen has during recent years received many promises of support in Euros from Italy as well as from the EU. The team has yet to receive many of the promised contributions. Ippolito's experience with many of the caimans

means, that Kite Gen today is a self-financing project, in spite of the fact that he himself and his co-workers have become much better at getting on in "the world of the caimans".

"Engineering students should also be taught how to communicate with public authorities," he concludes. The surplus from next year's production in Berzano di San Pietro is therefore earmarked to the development of bigger and better Kite Gens. "I will invest two million Euros and install three other machines, which can produce 9 megawatts. When we have six millions, we will install 10 machines. At this rate we will be producing 3 terawatts in 2020. What if Obama becomes aware of us in 2011 and orders 30 machines. It takes ever so little to get the show going..."

The hope is that Kite Gen will also be able to bring energy to those who spend all their energy on collecting water on foot. Ippolito sees his own future as being part of energy projects in developing countries. "Now we complete the project in Berzano di San Pietro. When the world realizes that it works, we will move on to the next level." While Ippolito talks

to us about his plans for the nearest future, he points to the yard behind the laboratory, where long steel pipes that will later become the "stalks" of the kites, are ready to be transported to the construction yard.

Back in the lab Ippolito applies a small kite model to demonstrate how sensors attached to the sides of the kite can show, control, and predict its movements up in the troposphere.

He also comes across a PowerPoint made a few years ago. It describes the world's energy consumption, taking its point of departure in his, his donkey's, and his dog's annual energy consumption. The graphic representations show that the race for food and the soil, on which to grow it, will begin for real in five years, if no drastic measures are taken. At this point figures and predictions fly through the air. If his impatient co-workers had not insisted on going for lunch, Ippolito would still be standing in front of the computer, explaining all the details about mega- and terawatts and the wind conditions of the troposphere, even though he emphasized on the phone that he had neither the time nor the inclination to be interviewed.

16/20
—
WHEN
EVERYTHING
HAS BEEN
WASHED
AWAY

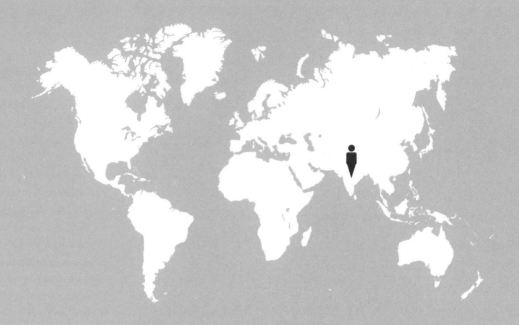

If the climate crisis fairy would grant you a single wish, you should wish for green investments to be profitable. If pension funds, investment funds, banks and traders in stocks and shares across the world felt that the best yields were created by investing money in fuel made from algae, protecting the rainforest, mobile gas plants to poor Indian families or kite energy, then that would really make a difference. "It's the economy, stupid," said Bill Clinton during the American election campaign in 1992 in order to emphasize that what it all boils down to is money. This also applies to the climate arena: it is the cash flow that determines the development and today it does not work for the climate. On the contrary.

However, the man who meets me in the lobby at the St. Regis Hotel on 5th Avenue

UDAY KHEMKA (1966)

—

Is the vice-president of the investment company SUN Group. He is particularly involved in sustainable investments. Furthermore he is the leader of the Khemka Foundation, one of India's major charity funds with special focus on anti-poverty strategies, education, children and youth. Uday Khemka has focused on the foundation's work with the climate and projects related to the environment. He is born in india and educated in Cambridge, Harvard, and Eton, and the World Economic Forum has named him as one of the 250 "Young Global Leaders".

—

in the centre of New York's most exclusive neighborhood intends to make a difference. He wants to mobilize the world's cash flow in gigantic efficient funds to the benefit of the climate and the people in the local areas, as well as the investors behind the funds. His name is Uday Khemka. He is a slight, well-dressed and forthcoming man in his 40s, one of India's most prominent financiers and philanthropists. He is often mentioned as one of the new global leaders. He is a man who personifies a new age and world order where North and South, new and old, rich and poor, East and West meet in new surprising constellations. He smiles and greets us with effusive politeness and is intensely preoccupied by the recent talks with business people and politicians at the annual Clinton Global

Initiative meeting. He invites us to join him in a quiet corner of the St. Regis luncheonette, a fashionable meeting place for rich business people from all over the world.

No place could be more appropriate for the meeting. Uday Khemka is a true globalist – born in India, educated at Eton, Cambridge, and Harvard, based in India, the USA, and England – and with the world market as his workplace. He is the next generation in one of India's large family dynasties, who owns a number of businesses and funds. In spite of his young age, he has had a long career in the investment business, having worked at Credit Suisse and Morgan Stanley. Today, he is the vice-president of the family owned company Sun Group's board of directors. He also runs the Khemka Foundation, which has specialized in anti-poverty programs and the environment. At the same time, Uday Khemka represents a new generation of financiers, men and women who are not content to just invest and harvest the results. The advent of the 2008 financial crisis made it clear to him and those similarly inclined that artificially inflated value and the scramble for short-term gains are not only risky to the individual, but will also have disastrous consequences to society.

For many years, the anti-poverty strategies and particularly the plight of the street children were Uday's main issue. However, in 2006 he participated in the annual meeting of the World Economic Forum for the world's financial establishment in Davos in Switzerland, where Al Gore gave a speech. "You may call it my 'Al Gore moment,'" he says and looks little embarrassed. "It occurred to me that virtually everything I do would be washed away, if we do not address this problem. It oc-

> ##
> IT OCCURRED TO ME THAT VIRTUALLY EVERYTHING I DO WOULD BE WASHED AWAY, IF WE DO NOT ADDRESS THIS PROBLEM.
> ##

curred to me, that this problem commands a scale and a size that makes all other problems seem insignificant," says Uday Khemka and points to three decisive factors that influence the lives of more than one billion inhabitants in India:

The Monsun: millions of people depend on the Monsun. If it moves just one degree away from the Punjab, "India's breadbasket", more than one billion will starve.

The glaciers: the Tibetan glaciers will risk collapsing. That will mean that the rivers will dry out, and hundreds of millions of people lose their water supply. The Ganges ensures the water supply of 250 million people. The Ganges might disappear.

The tsunami: in 2006 it struck millions of Indians. The risk was increased with the escalating climate change.

The jet-black long hair is brushed back in precise, smooth lines that remain fixed,

although he eagerly leans across the table in order to stress his points: "When I saw the world in that perspective, I also saw all of my good ideas in a new light. What is the good of being the smart microfinance guy, if a tsunami strikes? There are climatic tipping points. And there are turning points in the life of a human being. This was mine," he says.

Normally, we associate innovation with machines and laboratories. Uday Khemka's inventions concern money and cash flow. They are less visible, but just as important as wind turbines and LED light sources. In fact, we more or less know the price tag of "a stable climate": 200-350 billion dollars per year. This is the figure that the experts estimate that we must invest every year from 2020 in order to avail ourselves of the technologies that solve the problem. It sounds like an exorbitant figure, but as Uday Khemka's colleagues, the investment experts James Cameron and David Blood from Generation Investment have pointed out, the problem is not the money, but the direction of the cash flow – and the speed with which it should reach the green solutions. This is particularly important in the developing countries, which in 2020 will produce more than two thirds of the global emissions of CO_2. Uday Khemka has made it his mission to solve the problem by creating a "fund of funds" for green projects in developing countries. He has designed a mechanism that will pierce the dammed up capital and start the tidal wave.

Uday Khemka has invited a number of the world's wealthiest investors – pension funds, banks, investment companies – to join a partnership with the purpose of pooling streams of cash flow into one river with one specific purpose: to make it attractive to private investors in the rich world – e.g. the large pension funds – to invest in climate friendly infrastructures in the developing world. "The large developing countries and the rich countries must join forces in order to make economic growth in the large developing countries such as e.g. India sustainable. If we do not co-operate, it will be impossible. The poor countries in the south understandably enough argue that the start-up phase should be financed by the rich countries, because the poor countries have only just begun to fight poverty. So they say: "You must pay hundreds of millions of dollars every year. But we all know that the governments in the north do not have the mandates to do so. That is the central issue in the financing situation. That is our dilemma," says Uday Khemka and points to the fact that 85% of the climate investments must come from private sources.

"However, the strange thing is that the governments have never talked to the people who actually have the capital to solve the problem. In recent years I have gathered groups of institutional investors in the field of sustainability. And none of them have talked to the governments. The greatest money bins in the world. Nobody has talked to them! We found out a year and a half ago. However, these people actually think that investments in new green technologies and infrastructures are a good business for their pension fund clients. They are attracted to the concept. They would like to do it. But they complain that the chain of investors and the infrastructure is not yet in place."

The solution is to create five large regional infrastructures for investment funds which should invest in promising and climate friendly infrastructure such as plants pro-

MONEY, MONEY, MONEY
—
Uday Khemka works to create five very large regional funds that unite banks, investment companies, and pension funds in one purpose: channeling gigantic sums of private capital into green energy and green infrastructure projects in countries such as India and China. It should take place through public and private partnerships, where the governments of the developed countries are promised large private investments. However, these investments will only eventuate if they guarantee the relatively minimal extra means necessary to make the specifically selected green projects in the third world as economically attractive as other projects.
—

ducing renewable electricity, wind turbine parks, sun farms, and traffic systems. The funds should consist of local governments, infrastructure funds, regional banks, and private investors. In a joint effort they could, according to Uday Khemka, raise amounts in the vicinity of 15-25 billion dollars – in each region. Today promising climate projects in the region typically yield 2 percent below the amount that the investors would normally have as their target. However, according to Khemka the funds should address governments in the northern hemisphere such as the USA, the EU, and Japan and say: If you join a global climate agreement, then the climate

projects will probably yield another 1 percent surplus. Should you furthermore commit to adding the small, but important extra amount, which will ensure that the 15 percent becomes 16 percent, then that will trigger the enormous investments, that the funds can mobilize. "What we do is to build a bridge that spans 90 percent of the distance. And we tell the governments: please finance the remaining ten percent, then we can cross the bridge," says Uday Khemka.

But why does a successful, wealthy businessman in a pinstriped three piece suit get involved in the problems of the poor? "Ghandi stated it very clearly: the businessman is a worthy person entrusted with the means to fight for the community's welfare. In the north you talk about stakeholders. We do not. We talk about creating fantastic, successful and aggressively competitive companies that can generate so much value that we as a society can emerge from poverty," says Uday Khemka. He explains how the Indian businessman on a daily basis is confronted with suffering and poverty – and thereby with the incentive to create value in society. Every single time you stop at a red light, you see poverty through your windscreen. And he reminds us that these people, who have absolutely no agency in the creation of climate problems, are the ones who will be hit the hardest. When the rain fails, they will be the ones who pay the price.

"In the coming years this kind of thinking will spread in the investment sector. The value chain is taking shape. It is not a question if it will happen, but when. It has already begun. We experience it in our company. The investors are coming, and as long as co-operative efforts can be created between government and

> ❝
> **IF YOU ARE A
> BUSINESSMAN WITH
> JUST A FEW DECADES
> LEFT OF YOUR CAREER,
> THEN YOU WILL LOOK
> AT THIS AND SAY:
> I WANT TO BE IN IT!
> THIS IS THE GRANDEST
> STORY ABOUT
> WEALTH CREATION
> IN OUR TIME.**
> ❞

investors, and as long as we can solve some structural problems in the chain of investors, they will be willing to invest substantial sums. When we look back at this time, at the energy revolution and the fundamental changes it will bring to our economy, then we will realize that it was much more significant than for instance the IT revolution or the internet revolution. Those will look small in comparison. If you are a businessman with just a few decades left of your career, then you will look at this and say: I want to be in it! This is the grandest story about wealth creation in our time," says Uday Khemka.

*

Say the Word: Green!
According to the American patent office, the word
"green" occurred with the highest frequency in 2007
in connection with applications for new brands.
—

17/20
—
THE DESIGN HIPPIE

We are on our way to a park in the heart of Cape Town. The park is only a few hundred meters from Ewaldi Grové's office, but for an art and recycling buff like Ewaldi Grové the trip takes 20 minutes. Ewaldi Grové, 29, is South Africa's leading pioneer in the design of stylish furniture manufactured from waste products, which the rest of us would not dream of sitting in. Where most people se decay, slum, dirt and trash, she sees opportunities in shops, in the gutter and in the African metropolis' endless number of street vendors displaying animal figures, feather dusters, antiques and kitsch. When Ewaldi Grové finds an old hand mirror in a secondhand store, she smiles triumphantly. She is holding it in her hand, when we reach the park.

Ewaldi Grové has won several prizes for her ideas, not least the prestigious South

EWALDI GROVÉ (1980)

—

Graduated from The National School of the Arts in Johannesburg in 2004. She has a two year diploma education in interior design from the Greenside Design Center in Johannesburg, and a Cum Laude Btech degree in industrial design from the Cape Peninsula University of Technology from 2007.

—

African designer prize Golden Award at the Decorex fair in 2008. It all began with an insistent phone call one morning after a party in the home of her friend, the interior decorator Danielle Ehrlich. "One of Danielle's previous teachers asked her if she would give a talk on sustainability at the Decorex fair. The audience would mainly be architects and people interested in design," says Grové. The two designers joined forces and took on the challenge. They went on the Internet and did a lot of research into climate, design, and statistics. However, they quickly lost their way in technocratic terms and complex detailed knowledge. "Fortunately a friend dropped by and said: 'You are not teachers, you are artists. You should show what sustainability is - not tell it.' Of course the man was right. We should

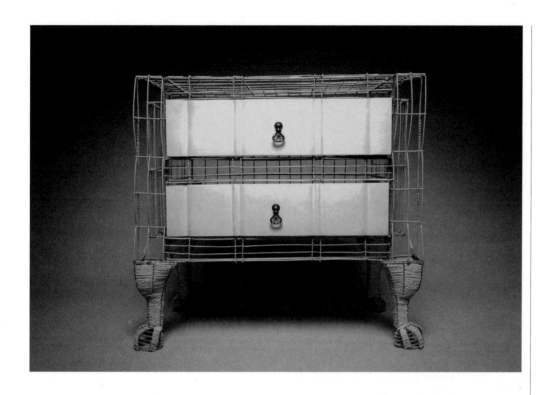

" WE WANT TO REBEL AGAINST THE CULTURE OF DISCARDING USED PRODUCTS AND CREATE A NEW CONSCIOUSNESS HERE IN SOUTH AFRICA AND IN THE REST OF THE WORLD. "

replace the statistics with issues that people could feel and touch."

They decided to produce an environmentally friendly collection, designing and producing 30 sustainable chairs in 30 days. Not only did they get very busy, they were also faced with an economic challenge. "We were down and out, and in such a situation how do you find materials for 30 new creations?" You search in the waste bins of a society characterized by an abundant supply of material goods. Ewaldi Grové and Danielle Erhlich went from backyard to backyard in the industrial neighborhoods of Johannesburg. They literally scavenged in the waste, looking for usable material. "We thought that there would be something we could use, and with which the factories would like to part."

In sustainable design, the materials used are central to the project. Instead of fresh wood, newly dyed textiles, metal and cast plastic, the designer finds natural materials, whose production does not require energy, or materials that others have discarded. Ewaldi Grové and her colleague changed the worthless materials and gave them cultural significance, exemplified by the small chest of drawers made from leftover steel wires – a reinterpretation of a classical piece of furniture found in almost all South African homes. Ewaldi Grové gestures with her hands and laughs, when she tells about all the garbage she managed to collect. Bits of wire, plastic wrappings, cardboard and bits of textile. "Fabulous," she says with a smile. The waste containers of the metropolis quite simply paved the road for the two women's de-

sign success. "However, we still had one problem. Now we had the ideas and the material, but we still had to transform it into an appealing design. For that we needed manual labor. The next step was to consider how we could draw on the resources of our local community, thereby contributing to its development."

According to the UN, 34 percent of the population of South Africa lives on less than two dollars a day and at least 25 percent are out of work. The African sector of the population represents the majority of the poor. Many black South Africans live in primitive townships consisting of huts made of sheet metal or discarded wood. The two designers went to the poor townships to search for people to recruit. They found poor, talented artisans who worked in miserable conditions.

1. Ewaldi Grové (right) and her designer colleague Danielle Erhlich. In a joint effort they have put sustainable design on the agenda in South Africa. Photo: Mikkel Andersen/Mayday Press

"We wanted to show them, that they could create more than standard souvenirs like wooden giraffes or key rings out of plastic pearls. And it was not difficult. None of us worked for anybody. We only worked together and for each other. Everybody was a part of the project and everyone believed in the idea. We struggled like mad and barely slept for thirty days," says Ewaldi Grové.

The objective was to create 30 pieces of furniture, but they only got half way through the project. Still, they were able to present a slideshow of unconventional furniture made out of recycled material to the visitors at the fair: a pillow stuffed with waste from a textile factory and a chair that looks like a bale of straw, but is actually made of strips of plastic – and the airy, elegant AfroDutch chest of drawers, which has since become a hit.

The day before the fair, the designers were chatting over a coffee. They were tired and not quite satisfied. "Why don't we start our own company – now, today – and get a stand at the fair with our furniture, instead of just giving a talk about how to make sustainable furniture design," says Ewaldi Grové. They followed up on the idea. With help from friends,

Ewaldi Grové is a South African pioneer in the field of furniture design based on the principle of sustainability. She works as a conceptual designer in the company Design Faktorii, and she uses only recycled material in her products. The furniture is mainly exported to Europe, the USA, and Australia, but the production creates jobs for people in South Africa.

—

the sales pitch stand was erected overnight. They had a sign printed with the name LIV DE-SIGN. As a credit for their effort, their furniture design received the fair's foremost recognition for innovative sustainable design.

Ewaldi Grové puts her hand on her heart and takes a deep breath in order to relive the experience she had at the ceremony, where she received the prize. The two young designers had taken on the challenge as an experiment. "We just wanted to show, that it is

■

**THE DRIVING FORCE BEHIND
GREEN INNOVATION ACCORDING TO
EWALDI GROVÉ**

–

**"The vision of creating a sustainable
and environmentally friendly design
and the vision of creating jobs in the
local community drive my innovation."**

–

"
RECYCLING IN ITSELF IS NOT ENOUGH. IT IS JUST AS IMPORTANT TO INVOLVE EVERYONE IN THE LOCAL COMMUNITY.
"

possible to make sustainable design. How-ever, suddenly we met agents, who wanted to export our products; we got lots of media coverage, were in the major design magazines and were called in for meetings. We were quite literally blessed from the outset," she says and lowers her voice a little.

"It was a fantastic experience to go out and show our artisans the magazines, which showed photographs of our furniture. Most of them have never been able to buy a glossy magazine. It was amazing to see their reactions and to hear them say: 'My work is in that photo.'"

Ewaldi Grové is hungry and invites me to a small café in the neighborhood. "This is a beautiful place, just look at all the colored pillows. And look: the chandeliers in the ceil-ing are made of recycled plastic bottles – how cool!" Today LIV DESIGN is an integral part of Design Faktorii, a well-established business with several subsidiaries in South Africa. Sustainability is still a key concept in Ewaldi Grové's design – but the difference between then and now is enormous. With representa-tion by Design Faktorii, her furniture and her message now reaches a much wider audience.

"It is amazing. We have the opportunity to create a lot of jobs for people who would oth-erwise not make very much money. We can be part of the process of changing the concep-tion of what a commodity is," says Grové. She wants to demonstrate that old can also be new, that old textiles can be beautiful, and that there is not necessarily a need for creating brand new products. "We want to rebel against the culture of discarding used products and create a new consciousness here in South Africa and in the rest of the world," she says. But if people begin to buy the furniture made by the two designers, they might also begin to discard their old bookshelves, couches and chairs? "I am aware of the problem. We are actually considering making a television program or an Internet blog in order to show people how they can repair and modernize their things. The purpose is to reach a balance between what we throw out and what we recreate. The challenging aspect of our art is to create designer furniture that people do not have the heart to throw out."

Ewaldi Grové realizes that it is not always easy to be sustainable. "I constantly challenge

myself. I am not the perfect consumer. If the Chinese shop sells the cheapest socks, then that is where I buy them. However, through my design I can fly the flag and represent a new standard. Sustainability is my drive. But recycling in itself is not enough. It is just as important to involve everyone in the local community."

Ewaldi Grové still thinks that she has a lot to learn and would like to apply knowledge from other disciplines in her design. Transport of a commodity is a source of considerable CO_2 emission and the young designer would like to co-operate with for instance engineers and find out how one can make it easier to transport the finished products, and thereby diminish the CO_2 emission. She also wants to learn more from the biological sciences about how to integrate nature in her work.

"Most of all I hope that a lot of people will see our idea and realize that recycled material does not necessarily look second hand and worn out. On the contrary. One can actually design furniture that looks like half a million out of things found in a waste container."

"
In terms of water and energy,
our basic goal is to re-establish the
environment and leave it as we found it.
All over the world we have freed up our
employees' energy and encouraged them
to produce ideas as to how we can reduce,
reapply, and re-establish the environment.
We are also making progress in our
efforts to lower the consumption
of water in our production and
our CO_2 emission.

> The result is that we generate incredible investments in all these environmental activities... Our returns are enormous. We attract new employees who are predominantly idealistic young people who have just graduated from university. They want to be part of an organization, where they work for a purpose, an organization which shows consideration for the coming generations.

"

Indra Nooyi
CEO, PepsiCo

18/20
—
THE NAME IS FISKER, HENRIK FISKER

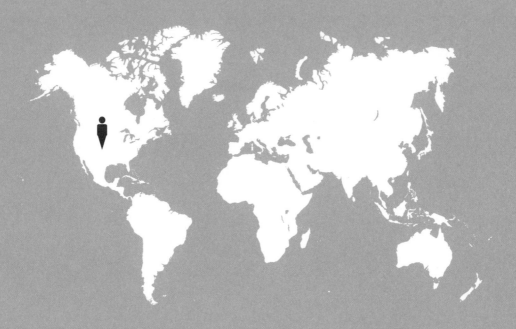

Henrik Fisker, managing director of Fisker Automotive, is standing next to the car Fisker Karma in the sunny lobby of the head quarter south of Los Angeles. With an affectionate gesture he runs his hand across the curves of the world's first four door plug-in hybrid car, ready to be mass produced. The term "Plug-in" means that it is ready to be recharged via an electrical outlet.

The car is low like a Porsche, long like a Mercedes, broad like a BMW, but the motor runs on electricity that propels it for the first 80 kilometers without using one drop of oil. Furthermore, it has solar cells on the roof, which supply electricity for the dashboard, the air-condition, and a few extra kilometers. Fisker Karma is a luxury car worthy of James Bond. Henrik Fisker defines the nature of the

1.

1. "It is always as if you have to suffer a little, sacrifice something, in order to be environmentally friendly. My cars settle that score," says Henrik Fisker, whose 400 horse power plug-in hybrid car accelerates from 0-100 kilometers per hour in 5.8 seconds and has a maximum speed of 200 kilometers per hour.

2. "I have difficulties writing because my jaw keeps dropping into the keyboard," an impressed reviewer said, when the Fisker Karma was presented to the public. The car's performance is benchmarked against Maserati and Jaguar models by a team of designers whom Henrik Fisker has handpicked during his twenty years in the car business. Just to give an example, the suspension has been developed by a Porsche designer, while a former Rolls Royce employee has developed the aluminum frame.

car in the following way: "This is a rebellion against people's prejudices that environmentally friendly cars are small, ugly golf cars that do 70 kilometers per hour and have a short range."

The production of the car will begin by the end of 2009. It will roll off the assembly line and service the first customers in mid 2010. This event will make Henrik Fisker the first man on the market with a plug-in hybrid car - six months earlier than General Motors' Chevy Volt, which will be on the road towards the end of 2010. On the coffee table

in the lobby lies a copy of Forbes magazine. It displays a photo of Henrik Fisker on the cover with the heading "The New Detroit". In the article the General Motors designer of the Chevy Volt, the car industry's legendary Richard Lutz, admits to being envious of Henrik Fisker: "He has solid financial backing. He has thousands of orders. His timing is completely perfect." Furthermore, the Fisker Automotive manager does not perceive the Chevy Volt as a competitor. "The Chevy? In principle it is just an Opel – a Volkswagen. There is a market for both of us. It is somewhat like comparing a gourmet

HENRIK FISKER (1963)

—

Graduated as a draughtsman in 1982. He drew sprinkler equipment for oilrigs, but dreamt of designing cars. He entered the Art Center College of Design in Switzerland and was later hired by BMW AG in Germany. He became managing director of BMW's Californian design center Design-Works and later creative director and leading designer in among others Ford's London Design Enterprise and Ford's Global Advance Design Studio in California. In 2005, he set up his own company Fisker Coachbuild, which among other products pro-duced specially refitted sports cars for Mercedes and BMW. In 2007, he joined forces with Quantum Tech-nologies and formed the company Fisker Automotive, which exclusively produces plug-in hybrid cars.

—

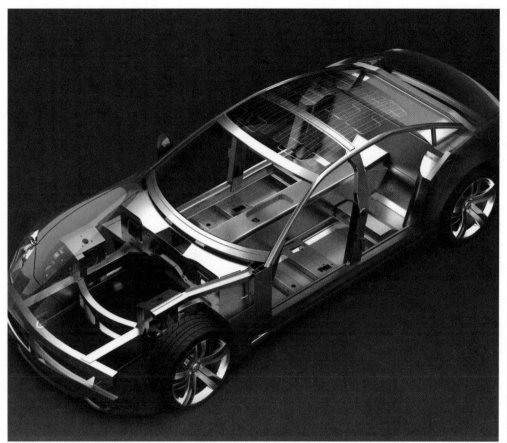

2.

restaurant to McDonald's. And naturally we are the gourmet restaurant," the CEO in the dapper suit says with a smile.

Henrik Fisker has not designed a green car for the masses. In response to the inevita-ble question why he has designed a vehicle, which in the USA will cost 81.500 dollars, Fisk-er explains: "When the first cell phone reached the market, the price was extremely high, because it was new technology. The same principle applies to the batteries in the plug-in hybrid cars. The price drops as the technology is refined. Furthermore, it is not my plan to

conquer the whole world," says the managing director from the car industry and ads that the market for luxury cars is still considerable. The economy version of Fisker Karma is on its way. Fisker Automotive has received a loan of 528 million dollars, guaranteed by the US Government, in order to develop a more fam-ily friendly plug-in hybrid car by the name of NINA. It will be half the price of a Fisker Karma. The ambitious plan is to produce 100,000 cars of this new and cheaper design per year from late 2012. "If we were to grow organically, it would have taken many years to reach such

a massive production level. It is the wish of the Ministry of Energy that we make our mark with a cheap plug-in hybrid car in order to signal American leadership. If the USA is not able to be at the forefront of this technological development, then we shall lose the defining edge of the future car industry," the Danish designer explains.

Like any American entrepreneurial company, Fisker Automotive also has private investors, some of whom are among the most successful venture capital companies in Sili-con Valley ever, including Kleiner Perkins who

THE FISKER CAR OF THE FUTURE
—

The Q-Drive plug-in technology will also be installed in the Fisker cars of the future. In 2011, the cabriolet version of Fisker Karma, the Karma Sunset, will be on the market. In 2012, the economy version NINA, which will cost around 42,000 dollars in the USA, will be launched. From late 2012, the yearly turnout should be 55 – 100,000 NINA models. That will be possible thanks to a loan of 528 million dollars granted by the American Ministry of Energy. This will make NINA an important element in the government's goal to have one million plug-in hybrid cars on the American roads by 2015. The ministry expects that the NINA project at best will create 5000 new jobs in the supply chain and at worst prevent that 5000 people employed by the supplier lose their jobs. Furthermore, thousands will be hired to produce plug-in hybrid cars in the USA. If the production and the sales plan works out as intended, Fisker cars will save 43,2 million barrels of oil in 2016.
—

> **THIS IS A REBELLION AGAINST PEOPLE'S PREJUDICES THAT ENVIRONMENTALLY FRIENDLY CARS ARE SMALL, UGLY GOLF CARS, THAT DO 70 KILOMETERS PER HOUR AND HAVE A SHORT RANGE.**

was always reputed to have an edge, when it comes to forecasting the next big trend. Just to give an example, the company was the first to invest in an unknown search engine on the Internet by the name of Google. However, Henrik Fisker does not lose any sleep over all these expectations. "I know that I am one of the best in the business. When people ask how I can sell 100,000 cars, then my answer is that my cars will be ten times cooler than all the others," he explains without hesitation and adds that he welcomes doubt. "Doubt means that you are onto something that has not been done before. We like to be the underdog."

It is evident that the 45-year-old car designer is comfortable in the steel and glass corner office with a view to the palms in the industrial park of Irvine in Southern California. Here he can set his own agenda. "When I designed petrol guzzling cars with V8 and V12

motors produced by the big car companies, I had no influence on the petrol economy itself. Now I do," he emphasizes and goes on to relate that the green adventure actually began with a conversation with Prince Albert of Monaco. At a car convention in 2006, Henrik Fisker asked Prince Albert if he would like to try out the seating of a Fisker Tranmonto, a specially redesigned Mercedes sports car from Fisker Coachbuild, a company that Henrik Fisker had just founded at the time. Prince Albert declined politely. "The Prince answered that his next sports car should be green. That set me off on a whole new train of thoughts," the car director says. He had already begun to worry about the future of car enthusiasts like himself. What would become of them the day the governments on a global scale, began to implement serious limits to CO_2 emissions? "Then I saw Leonardo Di Caprio arrive at the Oscar ceremony in a Toyota Prius. When a filmstar, who makes several million dollars a year, arrives in a small hybrid car, you can be sure that changes are occurring in the automotive industry," he says.

Later, Henrik Fisker met the manager of Quantum Technologies, a company that produces renewable energy solutions for the Pentagon. The company had invented a plug-in hybrid technology for a silent military vehicle that can position itself behind enemy lines without drawing attention to itself. It also performs with a swift acceleration, when the troops have to make themselves scarce. "Could this also be applied in a plug-in hybrid car?" asked Fisker. The manager of Quantum Technologies had not given this much thought, but the answer was yes. "When I saw Quantum's technology for the first time, it was like a revelation. I really felt I had found

GREEN CARS
—

The sports car Fisker Karma is run by an electric motor – the so-called Q drive, patented by Quantum technologies. For the first 80-90 kilometers, it is powered by a 22 kWh Lithium ion battery package. The car takes around four hours to recharge via an electrical outlet at home. If the trip is longer than 80 kilometers, a small petrol driven charger generator kicks in and generates electricity to the electric motor, while the energy generated from the brake system is redirected to the battery. The battery is replaceable and has an expected lifetime of around ten years. The acceleration time from 0-100 kilometers per hour is 5,8 seconds. The top speed is around 200 kilometers per hour. In the USA the price is 84,000 dollars – 420,000 DKK. The Fisker Karma is the first car on the market with solar cells on the roof. The cells supply electricity to the dashboard, cools down the inside of the parked car, and also ads around ten kilometers to the range of the battery per week, if parked outside. As an extra bonus Fisker Automotive also supplies solar cells to the garage roof, so that the electricity source of the battery is also green. 1500 Fisker Karma models have been preordered in the U.S. and will be sold through 45 suppliers. In Europe, a handful of importers will handle the sales. The goal is to produce 15,000 Fisker Karma cars per year from 2011.
—

> **"**
> # I WAS ALWAYS IN TROUBLE AT SCHOOL.
> # MY TEACHER TOLD MY FATHER RATHER BLUNTLY,
> # 'HENRIK WILL NEVER AMOUNT TO ANYTHING.
> **"**

a golden egg. Here was the opportunity to apply the force of a motor with the power of 400 horses and accelerate to 200 kilometers per hour – while still being environmentally friendly," says the enthused Henrik Fisker, who then forged ahead and founded Fisker Automotive in a joint venture with Quantum Technologies.

"I have realized many dreams in my life. However, every time I have done so, I have had to set a new and more advanced goal," says Henrik Fisker and relates that his Danish background also was decisive in terms of his choice to go green. "Denmark has never been a consumer society in the same league as the U.S. I was raised to switch off the light, when I leave a room and save on the resources." However, even though his native Denmark shaped the environmental consciousness of the 45-year-old managing director of a car company, it is "in spite of" and not "because of" his background that Henrik Fisker became a car designer. Henrik Fisker relates how his dream first manifested itself. "I was sitting on the backseat of my father's old Saab, when something that looked like a space ship suddenly

flew past the window. It was a Maserati. I knew then that I also wanted to design something so beautiful and exotic," he says with a twinkle in his eyes. At school Henrik always drew cars in all his notebooks. The result was that he did not get very good marks. "I was always in trouble at school. My teacher told my father rather bluntly, 'Henrik will never amount to anything.' The careers adviser told me that there was no such thing as a car designer. I could become an engineer or a draughtsman and I graduated as the latter," the Karma designer relates. He began his career drawing sprinkler systems for oilrigs. However, he felt no joy in this job and Henrik's father suggested that he should contact Volvo in Sweden and ask them how he could become a car designer. "I wrote to them, saying that I was ready to do whatever it takes. Sweep the floors, make coffee, that sort of thing," he says. Volvo replied that they sponsored an Art College of Design Center in Pasadena, California and that the school had just opened a branch in Switzerland. The hopeful draughtsman immediately threw his portfolio into the back of his small, rusty Alfa Romeo and drove south. "They could see that

I was talented. That was the first time anyone appreciated what I was good at," Henrik Fisker says. After three years in the school he graduated and went on to a comet career at BMW in Germany." I was a car designer. That was my first dream come true.

The next dream I realized was when my car, the BMW Z8 was in a James Bond movie," says Henrik Fisker and relates how he had to pinch himself at the sight of Agent 007 driving his design on the big screen. "To think that little Henrik from Allerød [a Copenhagen suburb],..." the manager says and shakes his head. In 2005, he started his own company Fisker Coachbuild, which is now exclusively a design centre for Fisker Automotive.

While Henrik Fisker relates his dreams, he gives us a tour of the head quarters. On the design floor there are co-workers as well as interns from the Harvard School of Design. They are sketching in an open-plan office populated by countless notice boards with photos of everything from peacocks to silver cutlery. Next to a full size clay model of a Fisker Karma, you find a fully developed cabriolet version of a plug-in car by the name of Sunset. It will

**THE DRIVING FORCE BEHIND
GREEN INNOVATION ACCORDING TO
HENRIK FISKER**

—

■ **Seeking new and more advanced
goals**
■ **Making cooler products than the
competitors**

—

be on the market in 2011. "I think about cars
round the clock, how the light is reflected in
their curves, how the lines meet," says Henrik
Fisker and begins to talk about the wooden
panels in the interior. The wood does not
originate from a rain forest, but from oak and
walnut trees that have been salvaged from the
large forest fires in California. "This exemplifies how we try to incorporate a green agenda.
There is no reason to cut down more trees, if
we already have ideal material right in front of
us," he says as we walk past sketches of Fisker
Automotive's new NINA model. It has been
named after Christopher Columbus' ship. The
idea was to symbolize the changes in the car
industry from the old world of fossil fuels to
the new green agenda.

1. Henrik Fisker wanted to make a radically
different car. "The hybrid cars on the market today allow you to save perhaps 15-20
percent. However, with my car 80 percent
of the population will be able to travel to
and from work without using any petrol at
all," he says.

1.

THE PERSPECTIVE OF **ETERNITY**

—

Our memory span and perceptive abilities often get the better of us. We automatically conclude that our daily perceptions represent normality. Such is our make-up. However, in an historical perspective things look different-ly. Jack Steinberger, Nobel laureate in physics and Director of CERN in Switzerland travels the world with this diagram, developed by his colleague Chris Llewelyn Smith. It shows humanity's consumption of fossil fuels in a perspective of 12.000 years. Until a few hundred years ago we did not use coal, oil, and gas. And in less than 100 years we will have stopped using these fuels completely. Partly because there will probably only be enough oil and gas left for another 30-35 years and coal for another 60 years. Partly because these fuels destroy the living conditions on Earth. The

88-year-old Steinberger has a unique perspective on the climate problem. In his lifetime the Earth's population has tripled and the energy consumption has increased eight-fold.

Picture
Nobel laureate and Director of CERN in Switzerland, Jack Steinberger – photographed in 1963 For LIFE magazine.

Illustration
Consumption of fossil fuels in an historical perspective
—
The graphic illustration shows the human consumption of fossil fuels over a span of 12,000 years.

-4000   -3000   -2000   -1000   0   1000   2000   3000   4000   5000   6000   7000   8000

19/20
—
BLUE
IS THE NEW GREEN

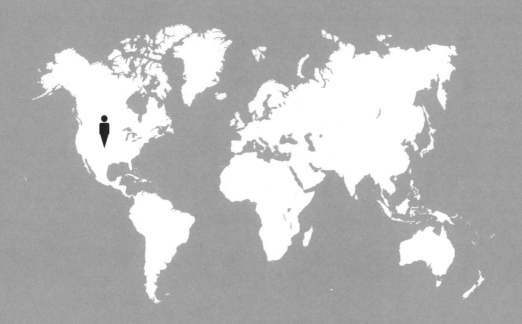

"Could this spoon stop global warming?" Adam Werbach looks inquiringly through the holes in the handle of a plastic spoon. He quickly answers his own question: "Of course not. But it is an important first step." The 36-year-old manager of the consultancy firm Saatchi & Saatchi puts the spoon down on a table made out of a slice of a tree trunk. In enthusiastic terms he relates that the new spoon contains 13 percent less plastic. The spoon is a sales success in Wal-Mart, the world's largest retail chain. Every week 127 million customers shop in Wal-Mart and the annual turnover exceeds the individual GDP of 144 countries.

"When we operate on a scale of that size, then the effect of the slightest change is enormous. Imagine how much oil such a small change saves," he says. Wal-Mart is one of the

ADAM WERBACH (1973)
—

Has a BA in political science from Brown University. At University he founded the Sierra Student Coalition, a sector for younger members of the Sierra Club, America's largest environmental movement. Later, he became president of The Sierra Club. Towards the end of the 1990s, Adam Werbach founded his own consultancy company Act Now Productions, which helped companies implement sustainability strategies. He was also co-founder of the Apollo Alliance whose goal is to kick start an economy based on sustainability. In 1994, he made his famous speech "The Death of the Environmental Movement". Subsequently, he began co-operating with Wal-Mart on issues of sustainability. In 2008, Saatchi & Saatchi S (S for sustainability) bought Act Now Productions, thereby becoming the world's largest consultancy agency in the field of sustainability. Adam Werbach has the global responsibility for the company. Besides Wal-Mart, giants such as General Mills, Procter & Gamble, Nike, and Xerox are among the companies in the client portfolio and their cumulative annual turnover is around one billion dollars.
Adam Werbach is the author of the books *Act Now, Apologize Later* and *Strategy for Sustainability*.
—

> **IN OUR EAGERNESS TO PROTECT BABY SEALS AND REDWOOD FORESTS WE HAVE FORGOTTEN THE HUMAN BEING. IF WE CANNOT ALIGN SUSTAINABILITY AND CLIMATE CHALLENGES WITH THE AVERAGE AMERICAN'S HOPES AND DREAMS ABOUT HIS OR HER FUTURE, THEN WE HAVE LOST.**

many clients in Saatchi & Saatchi's company portfolio that the company advises on sustainability, communication, and PR. In that order. That means that a company's sustainability strategy must be incorporated in the company's daily routines. It should not be an add-on in deference to global climate concerns. "The triple bottom line does not make sense," says Adam Werbach, referring to modern business philosophy, where one does not only keep an eye on the economy on the bottom line. One is also aware of the company's social and environmental responsibility. "I have never yet met a managing director who includes the survival of the planet in his turnover, when he presents the quarterly accounts – by then it's too late. If sustainability is not an integrated part of the growth strategy, then it will just be an empty buzzword," says Adam Werbach.

We are in San Francisco, California on the American West Coast, where narrow, steep streets lead us to the Potrero Hill Quarter. Here

you find the narrowest and most windy street in the city. This is where the gold prospectors settled in their day. When the gold rush was over, the gold diggers built shipyards, slaughterhouses, and bakeries and developed an iron industry. Today, most factory buildings have been turned into residential housing and state-of-the-art offices. In this trendy area, you find Saatchi & Saatchi S sustainability centre.

A few years ago, nobody had imagined that Adam Werbach would be the manager of this office. He is the former president of The Sierra Club, America's largest and oldest association for the protection of the environment. At the tender age of 23, the dynamic activist was handpicked to sit at the helm of the organization which at the time counted one million members. Prior to that, he had founded the Sierra Student Coalition, a branch of younger members. Towards the end of the nineties, he was part of the leading echelon in a generational change that meant that the organization

expanded its target strata of society. Previously, it had consisted mainly of the white, slightly older section of the middle class. After two years as manager, Adam Werbach had succeeded in lowering the average age from 47 to 37 years. However, he was not content to rest on his laurels. In 2004, he made a speech that sent shock waves through his hinterland. In the controversial speech, he declared that the environmental movement was dead. Then he performed an autopsy with an edge. Bush had just been elected for another four years in The White House and the left, complete with environmental activists, democrats, and NGOs had lost what Werbach calls "the war of ideas". "In our eagerness to protect baby seals and redwood forests, we have forgotten the human being. If we cannot align sustainability and climate challenges with the average American's hopes and dreams about his or her future, then we have lost," he said in the speech and emphasized that the right wing had devel-

A BLUE STRATEGY FOR SUSTAINABILITY
—

In the blue strategy Adam Werbach and Saatchi & Saatchi S combine sustainability with the growth of a company. As opposed to green, blue encompasses not just the environment, but also the social, cultural, and economical aspects of sustainability. Read more and test just how blue your own lifestyle is on: www.strategyforsustainability.com
—

oped an excellent communication strategy by equating the combat of the greenhouse effect with the loss of jobs and quality of life.

"In those days, the debate still raged between climate versus jobs. Fortunately, the last three years have seen the arrival of a new paradigm. However, at the time the speech did not do much for my popularity," he says with a wry smile. By making the speech, he had committed hara-kiri in terms of forwarding his career. The phone rang nonstop. Colleagues, old friends, and politicians wanted to tell him just how wrong he was. The board of the environmental group Common Assets fired him from his position as manager. He was now without a job and had just become the happy father of a newborn daughter. "I remember thinking: What will I do now – become a firefighter?" The Saatchi & Saatchi manager raises both arms and moves forward on his chair. Most of all, his office resembles a comfortable log cabin with furniture made from untreated wood and deep armchairs in retro orange.

Then Wal-Mart called. The management had read his speech with interest and wanted him to help create a new strategy for sustainability. In his book *Act Now, Apologize Later* he had castigated the chain and called the discount concept a poison that destroys city after city by paying low wages to the employees and the suppliers who are forced to compromise in order to keep prices down. First, Werbach declined. "I did not think that Wal-Mart was serious about their offer, and I feared that they would just feed me into their PR machine. Still, I could see that they would make a difference by realizing just one percent of their plans." So he gave Wal-Mart a chance.

At first, Adam delegated homework. The management were to meet CO₂ experts, read climate reports and visit visionary, sustainable projects. To his great surprise, the managers of the supermarket chain did as they were told. Then it was Werbach's turn to learn. He participated in the company's quarterly meetings and here there the advice to the local branch managers was extremely straightforward: In future, they would be assessed and awarded bonuses based on improvements of the sustainability of their branch. That was the decisive moment. "I understood that this was not an attempt to 'greenwash' their brand," he says. And in the same breath he relates that there are plenty of companies in this category. If the autopsy speech had downgraded Adam Werbach's popularity among the environmentalists, then his new job at Wal-Mart aroused hatred. "Many people have a static view of 'good and evil'. However, I want to do everything in my power to face up to the climate change – including reconsidering old principles," he insists.

These days, Wal-Mart has three ambitious goals in terms of sustainability: 100 percent recycling of waste from the retail chain's outlets and 100 percent renewable energy supply to the branches. Furthermore, in 2012, 95 percent of all the goods on the shelves must meet the standards of a so-called sustainability index. Among other variables this is based on an analysis of the product's strain on environment and climate from cradle to grave. However, the products must still be cheap – people do not shop in Wal-Mart in order to be environmentally friendly, but to save money. "When Wal-Mart began to put pressure on their suppliers, it turned out that many products actually become cheaper as they go greener. Less packaging will for instance result in enormous savings," says Werbach.

The next step was to make the consumers aware of the fact that their choice of products makes a difference. Werbach decided to turn the 1.3 million employees into ambassadors of a sustainable lifestyle and thereby into role models for the rest of the American population. 90 percent of all Americans shop in Wal-Mart annually. In broad terms, the employees are recruited from the segment from which the environmental organizations never quite managed to recruit. They have little education, get minimum wages, and have more diseases resulting from their life styles than the rest of the population. They live far away from Werbach's progressive hometown of San Francisco, where there is an ecological coffee shop on every street corner. "We must take our point of departure in the individual lives of the customers. If we are not pleased with our own lives, then it becomes difficult to care about the survival of the planet," says the manager.

Werbach and his colleagues travelled to all the Wal-Mart branches in the country in order to present a voluntary employee program called PSP – Personal Sustainability Project. Every employee should find an area in his or her life which was not sustainable, and then do something about it. It could be anything from changing your diet to transport, waste disposal, and smoking. The program is a voluntary grassroots program, where employees in the local outlets volunteer as PSP captains and assist colleagues in carrying out their PSPs. "We call it nano practice. Replace your old light bulbs, park your car in a parking space far from your destination and walk the rest of the way, cook one ecological meal per week. Do something that is good for you, for your society, and for the planet," says Werbach.

Four years after declaring the American environmental movement dead, he gave another major speech, "The Birth of Blue", where he introduced a definition of a new sustainable popular movement that he called blue – predicting that blue will replace the green movement. The blue movement integrates social, cultural, economic, and environmental aspects. "A cashier's 11-year-old daughter was detained at school because she refused to throw out a plastic bottle in recess time. She was inspired by her mother's PSP concerning recycling, but the school had no recycling program. When her mother heard about this, she became so furious that she went to talk to the mayor. Today, all the municipal schools have a recycling program," Werbach said among other things in his blue speech.

Three years after the program was launched, 400,000 employees still apply their PSP. And Adam Werbach's own PSP? That is to cook healthy breakfasts for his children – and to learn something from them every day.

THE DRIVING FORCE BEHIND GREEN INNOVATION ACCORDING TO ADAM WERBACH

—

■ Global warming is the most comprehensive catastrophe humankind has ever had to face.

■ I am not a tourist on this planet. By turning sustainability into the motor of corporate growth and human lifestyles, I hope that we will still be able to save the planet.

—

1. Four years after Adam Werbach in a controversial speech in *The Commonwealth Club* in San Francisco declared the environmental movement dead, he returned to the same platform and launched a new – not green, but blue – concept. It signifies a way of including sustainability in contexts familiar to the average American.

1.

20/20
—
THE KITE
RUNNER

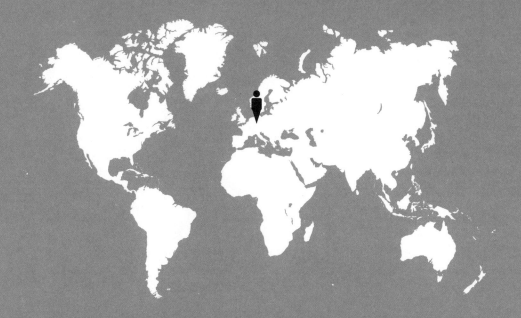

Stephan Wrage is running along the beach with his kite. The wind is strong and his kite almost drags him across the sand. He is 15 years old. He feels the enormous pull of the kite's string between his fingers, and at that moment an idea is born. Today Stephan Wrage is 37. He still flies kites. He is an engineer and in his Hamburg based company, SkySails, he has long since put the idea that came to him on the beach into operation,.

The idea behind the SkySails concept is to attach a gigantic, electronically controlled kite – or a sail – to the large, heavy freighters and container ships, and then harness the pull which the kite creates. It is a simple concept which combines ancient and brand new technology. It consists of a string, a sail, and an advanced, electronic launch and control system.

STEPHAN WRAGE (1972)

—

Is an engineer, a yachtsman, and a kite runner. In 2001, he founded the company SkySails. During the first year, the company received entrepreneurial support in Hamburg, and later it partnered with two German shipping companies, Beluga Shipping and Wessels Reederei.

—

More than 150 years ago the large sailing ships on the seven seas were replaced by the steam ships. In the beginning, the ships applied steam as well as sails, but soon the sails were discarded, and the steam engine took over completely. Following steamships, the efficient combustion engines arrived, propelling ships, tankers, and container ships and taking over the shipping business. Today, sailing ships and sailboats are relegated to sports and leisure activities. However, Stephen Wrage and SkySails have automated the process of setting sails. By pressing a button, the captain can project the sail into the sky and pull it down again. The 160 square meter kite sail shoots into the sky to a height of 100 – 300 meters above the wave crests. At this altitude, the sails will catch much stronger winds than those on a traditional mast. Once projected into the sky, the sail unfolds and

SAIL ON BIG SHIPS

—

SkySails is a system that consists of a kite sail designed for small and large ships with combustion engines. An ultra-light kite sail of 160 square meters is launched and then controlled electronically from the ship. The sail has a tractive force which under the right wind and weather conditions corresponds to that of an Airbus A318 motor. A 120 meter freighter will on average be able to save between 10 and 35 percent fuel per day. A daily saving of 2,5 tons of fuel equals 5000 DKK per day in operating costs.

—

catches the wind, which is stronger and more constant than the winds propelling the ship at sea level. An autopilot controls the movements of the sail and places it in a position where it exercises the maximum pull in relation to the ship's course and the direction of the wind.

"When you introduce an idea, which is so new and different, you encounter a lot of skepticism and opposition," says Stephan Wrage, kite runner and enthusiastic yachtsman. "In spite of skepticism and raised eyebrows at the beginning of the project, SkySails took off." The first challenge was to find a shipping company with pioneering spirit and the courage to have an open mind," says Stephan Wrage. In 2001, shortly after founding the company, SkySails succeeded in getting a contract with two German shipping companies, Beluga Shipping and Wessels Reederai. They were interested

> ❞
> ## IT IS A SIMPLE FACT: WIND IS CHEAPER THAN OIL AND THERE IS PLENTY OF IT ON THE HIGH SEAS. FURTHERMORE, IT DOES NOT PRODUCE EMISSIONS OF ANY KIND.
> ❞

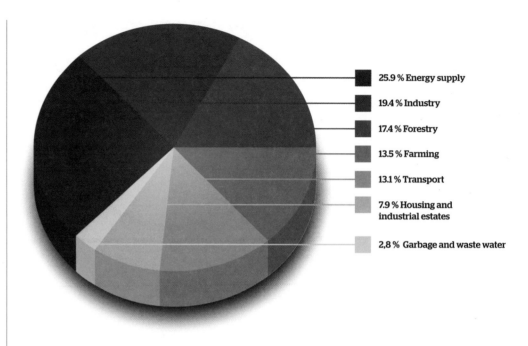

25.9 % Energy supply

19.4 % Industry

17.4 % Forestry

13.5 % Farming

13.1 % Transport

7.9 % Housing and industrial estates

2,8 % Garbage and waste water

Illustration
Global CO₂ emission distributed
in a pie chart. Source: IPCC 2007

in participating in the testing and the development of the kite sail.

The next challenge was to find sponsors and investors. "That demanded an intense and prolonged work effort," says Stephan Wrage. "It was particularly challenging during the period where we developed the technology and needed continual contributions in order to be able to forge ahead." However, the shipping companies were interested, and a couple of large, solvent investors came along and saw the opportunities the project represents. The individual shipping companies may stand to gain large profits. They can save enormous amounts of fuel and money, as well as CO₂. The 133 meter long freighter *Beluga SkySails* tested the sail for a year and a half on several transatlantic voyages. On the sail's virgin voyage,

the ship used only 20 percent of the machine power it normally needs to cross the Atlantic. That corresponds a fuel saving of 20 percent. Under favorable wind and weather conditions, a freighter could save up to 50% of its machine power. On average, the sail supplies a motive power that equals the motor in an Airbus A318.

There are around 100,000 freighters on the seven seas and 95 percent of the world's trade crosses the oceans. International marine transportation represents 4,5 percent of the planet's cumulative CO₂ emission. Most large ships use a much cheaper and more polluting fuel called bunker oil. It consists of the sediment that is left, when petrol and other more valuable substances have been extracted from the oil. Lately, it has become evident that the international marine traffic emits much more

CO₂ than previously assumed. This fact puts pressure on the shipping companies and the trade as such.

Stephan Wrage is convinced that his idea is not only financially advantageous to the shipping trade and his own company. It is also sustainable. "it is a simple fact that wind energy is cheaper than oil. There is plenty of it on the high seas – and it does not create emissions of any kind! SkySails has the potential to make a significant and important contribution to the combat of climate change. As a company, we would like to be an example of how you can create a successful business by working with nature – and not against it," says Stephan Wrage.

Freighters, container ships, and trawlers of up to 120 meters, which travel at the

speed of 10 to 18 knots, will benefit the most from SkySails, given the present technology. However, SkySails is in the process of refining the technology and developing larger and more efficient sails. The company's next step is to conquer the global market. For this reason, the SkySails Company's next step will be to launch a series or a mass production of the kite system. At the moment, the Wessels Reederei is building three new freighters in Slovakia and these are all fitted with the Skysails system which is ready to use from day one. Stephan Wrage and SkySails have created a joint venture with Zeppelin Power Systems, a strong player in the worldwide marine equipment business. Stephan Wrage is counting on the new partnership to make the kite sail an important factor on the sea.

THE PERFECT STORM

When you consider the challenges we will be facing as a civilization in the coming decades, there can be no doubt: we need to create *the perfect storm*. We need all green ideas to merge and form a synthesis in a way that surpasses everything we have seen so far. We need the sharpest brains to perform with excellence and disseminate their ideas to the rest of us. We need a lot of them in all corners of the global village. We need their ideas to cross-pollinate – and we need all this to happen as quickly as possible.

In the most authoritative investigation so far into what is needed in order to solve the climate crisis, McKinsey & Co conclude with the utmost simplicity: We must apply all the solutions we know sooner rather than later and in every corner of the globe, including poor countries like India, in order to reach our goal. Until 2009 most experts felt that it would be sufficient if the rich parts of the world took a giant leap forward. However, that will not be enough. Electric cars, low energy houses, and solar energy plants must also be installed in the poor sectors of the globe.

A number of significant preconditions are in place – or will soon be. In the first instance more and more countries realize that those who check in first with the smart solutions will win. India is an encouraging example. Since 2008 the Indian government has changed strategy. Previously all rhetoric revolved around India's role as a victim of climate change – which is quite understandable.

However, since 2008 the government has also made an effort to develop climate solutions for the benefit of a population, of whom 400 million do not have access to electricity. Several of the innovators in this book exemplify the new attitude. As the Indian climate expert Malini Mehra from the Center for Social Markets reminds us: "We have successfully changed the victimization story of India as a passive spectator with increasing CO_2 emission. We have pursued an agenda of opportunities, which deals with green jobs and growth for the many, not just for the few. We have found support in important sectors of the business world. The support has enabled us to perform a swift readjustment to competitive, climate friendly growth. We have stressed the fact that

> **ONE DAY OUR CHILDREN WILL LOOK US IN THE EYE AND ASK: 'WHAT DID YOU DO, WHEN YOU REALIZED HOW BAD IT WAS?' I WOULD LIKE TO BE ABLE TO ANSWER: I DID EVERYTHING I COULD.**

Shai Agassi,
CEO and founder of Project Better Place
—

taking action against climate change is also a proactive strategy against poverty and for development.

However, in the global perspective there is a long way to go. The 1,000 terawatt question is:

How do you create the frameworks which will change the present wave of green innovation into a tsunami? What would it take to create 100 green Nobel laureates in ten years? How do we design the perfect environment to foster the Pasteurs, the Da Vincis, the Darwins, and the Einsteins of the climate age?

You will find part of the answer by listening to the innovators portrayed in this book. In the first instance a number of obvious barriers to green innovation should be removed as quickly as possible. Our main problem is the way that we price energy. In spite of almost four decades of explicit scientific knowledge of the fact that the burning of fossil fuels damages our ecosystems, the world's cheapest energy resource is still coal. And after coal we have oil and gas. The three most damaging types of energy are the cheapest. The least harmful – renewable energy from sun, water, and wind – are the most expensive. Of course there is a reason why mature technology such as coal winning is cheaper than an advanced, new technology such as solar energy, but there is also a reason why we have states and legislation. For centuries the state has promoted rules that direct the development of society in the right direction. Nevertheless, we have as yet only to a limited extent applied classical political tools such as fees, taxes, and subsidies in order to punish the wrong solutions and reward the good.

We have not yet made it clear that there should be a cost of dumping greenhouse gasses in the atmosphere. In our economic system we factor costs for salaries, commercials, transport, and raw materials into the price of goods, but we forget the costs of damages to our ecosystems. Economists talk about "externalities", the costs that are not factored into the price of a product or a service. We know more or less what natural damages will ensue, if we emit for example 1 ton of CO_2. However, the car manufacturer or the entrepreneur need not worry about that. Society does not demand that you pay for that. It is free. The British have a wonderful word for such structures. They call them "perverse".

This corresponds to a scenario, where it would be legal for everyone to throw their waste out of the window. When it comes to CO_2 emission, nobody punishes you, nobody demands that you behave or that you dispose of your waste in a responsible way, pay the garbage collection fees, or take your refuse to the dump.

A significant cause might be that CO_2 is invisible. Some years ago the British Environmental Protection Agency made a movie, where they via digital techniques visualized the CO_2 emission from airplanes, cars, and pylons. It looked like a mixture of smoke and steam. The result was frightening. The air above the pylons danced like a 20 meter tall wildfire, the spaghetti motorways were covered in a fog that looked like a heat haze, and the jet motors of an airplane taking off left a gigantic slipstream of poisonous particles. In terms of economy we have pretended that these emissions do not exist. Lord Nicholas Stern, possibly the world's foremost climate economist, has called this phenomenon "the greatest market error in history."

Of course one can find examples of progressive people attempting to change the status quo. In Germany, for instance, the politicians have for years favored solar energy and Denmark has focused on wind energy. The results are outstanding, and today Germany is the global leader in solar energy (even if the sun is not that strong in the South of Germany) and Denmark leads in wind energy. However, these initiatives are delimited to two countries, where they have neither been implemented consistently nor with particularly significant rewards for the environmentally friendly conduct.

At the moment the EU is carrying out the greatest experiment in climate economics to date. In 2007 the EU introduced the so-called Emissions Trading Scheme (ETS). This entails that the member states and their top energy consuming companies are now subjected to caps on their CO_2 emissions. Every country and every company has a quota which equals permission to emit a certain number of tons of CO_2. If a company wants to emit more CO_2 than its quota permits, then the company can purchase the necessary quota from another manufacturer, who economizes on energy and therefore has quotas to spare. In this way a CO_2 emission market is created, and the people who save on emission will be able to profit. In the USA similar systems have a history of successfully reducing the emission of among other substances sulphur dioxide. However, if this were to work, the price of a CO_2 quota must of course be high enough to encourage people to save on emission. The present price of approx. 20 US dollars cap per ton is too low. It should probably be tripled in order to take effect. Furthermore, the CO_2 emission should be sufficiently low. Both measures have still not been implemented in the EU, and for this reason the green heroes of Europe continue to work for the green cause against many odds.

When the inventors come up with a non-polluting type of energy, the green feature still does not add to the value in significant ways. It will be a long time before green energy can compete with coal combustion, which we continue to allow, regardless of the price the planet will have to pay. Of course the imperative "follow the money" also goes for innovation. If we want to create the perfect storm in green innovation, we must make it more attractive to go green. It must be profitable. What else do we need to do?

We could ask the people who innovate and invest enormous sums in research, development, and demonstration projects. The world's leading companies often have research budgets that exceed the budgets of some countries. Given the opportunity to have a thirty minute face-to-face conversation with the world's heads of state, what would the innovators say? Actually we know the answer. In later years companies such as General Electric, Microsoft, and Tata have joined forces and prepared a priority list, where some central messages occur.

Here are The Six Commandments, which could give any politician a green conscience:
■ **Put a price on pollution.** It should cost to destroy the atmosphere with greenhouse gasses. Developing non-polluting technologies must be rewarded. Make it attractive and advantageous to be the person who first comes up with the best solution.
■ **Introduce a CO_2 emission cap.** Then lower it gradually – but in good time – till it is sufficiently low to prevent dangerous changes in the climate. Communicate this in no uncertain terms to the business community and to the researchers, so they know where they stand, when they invest and plan.
■ **Give the individual countries and/or the most polluting companies a pollution permission with a ceiling a little below their present pollution and then lower it gradually.** Allow trade with the permits to the extent that those who save CO_2 will be able to sell their surplus to those who cannot stay within the limits of their permit.
■ **Design the carbon market as a comprehensive global network.** That means implementing a co-operation between all countries, involving all sectors and all emissions of greenhouse gasses.
■ **Make a long-term, strategic priority of the public funds allocated to research and technology development.** That will create certainty among other investors and thereby get the private sector to double the amount manifold.
■ **Make sure to allocate significant subsidies not just to research and development, but also to the final critical transition from idea to market**

There are a number of other measures, which will also stimulate green innovation. However, The Six Commandments constitute the winning conditions for accelerating the global green boom, which is in the making.

Considering the level of danger to the planet, the catalogue above is rather modest in its demands. Nobody is demanding full government support or that democracy be abolished. The innovators and the companies quite simply ask for *encouragement and certainty*. The more the governments encourage advantageous behavior, for instance by allocating subsidies and giving inexpensive loans, and punish untoward conduct, for example with dues and demands, the more money the business community will automatically invest in green innovation. This is what you call price signaling. The stronger the signal, the more innovation you get. At this point we should bear in mind that approx. 85 US dollar out of every 100 US dollar invested in green technology come from the private sector. The ministers of the environment and the university professors do not pay for the development of the next smart windturbine; the business world does. And if the guys in the lab know there is money to be made, then things begin to happen.

And certainty means that the bosses in charge of the men and the women in the lab, as well as the directors of technology, innovation, or research, will be in a position to know in advance what framework their research can expect. Through a global climate agreement the politicians may be able to help these people. In the first instance they will be able to make long term agreements about the regulation of CO_2 emission. One could for example make agreements that reach 10-20-30 years into the future, instead of agreements that have to be renegotiated every fourth year (such as e.g. the Kyoto agreement). In this way it would be much easier for the technology director to go to the board and ask for money to develop a new gadget, which may be ready in 3-5 years. He does not have to worry that it will be superfluous by next Christmas, because the rules by then will have changed or the market will need a completely different type of device.

Furthermore, the politicians will be able to establish benchmarks. One could for example envision goals for how many kilometers a car should run per liter, how well a house should be insulated, or how much CO_2 a certain industry should be allowed to emit. Such benchmarks have a tendency to sharpen not just the managers' talent, but to a great extent also the capabilities of the people working in the labs. The goals could even be dynamic: Every year the energy consumption of the electrical devices must be reduced by 10%. This will also bring out the best in the creative brains. "Companies are particularly good at competing against each other in order to be the first to reach a goal. Tell us what we must achieve and when. Then we go for it. And usually we reach the goal," says Steen Riisgaard, director of the Danish biotech company Novozymes. He knows what he is talking about. Novozymes invented the enzymes, which today make it possible for all of us to wash our clothes at 30 degrees or even in cold water. Just think of the number of washing machines around the world and imagine the energy we can save, when we all switch from 60 or 90 degrees to 30 or 0.

In 2009 the American magazine *The Atlantic* published a thought-provoking article with the title "The Elusive Green Economy". The author, Joshua Green, had reread an article published by *The Atlantic* in 1977. At the time Jimmy Carter had just moved into The White House and had done some research in order to compare 1977 with 2009. It turned out that the situation 32 years ago represented an uncanny parallel to the present-day scenario in the USA. A new idealistic president had come into office. He was swept along by a wave of enthusiasm. He felt strongly about climate and environment and was encouraged by the trend-setting group of scientists, who already at that stage (!) predicted that a continued combustion of fossil fuels would create a greenhouse effect with serious consequences. He announced that massive investments in green technology were imminent. He put pressure on the Congress to pass environmental laws that would make a difference. The American venture capitalists and technologists were excited about green tech. The president even installed a solar panel on the roof of the White House. It was blowing up for a perfect storm.

However, four years later, Jimmy Carter lost the election and a new president, Ronald Reagan, came into office. He did not support extreme phenomena such as renewable energy and environmental protection. The political signals changed. A whole range of environmental laws were revised, and in a matter of a few years the green tech euphoria and the green dollars were gone. In a symbolic gesture Reagan even removed the solar panel from the roof of The White House.

The wind of the perfect storm died down. In the article Joshua Green speculate on the fatal consequences of the political zigzag course: Take a second to consider what the world would have looked like today if Jimmy Carter's vision of an American energy policy had been allowed to unfold since 1977: The world would have benefitted from 32 years of green activities! A well-funded powerhouse would have provided full momentum to the legendary American innovation machine, resulting in decades of enterprising activities among Californian investors, technology developers, and universities... In hindsight it is frightening and depressing to think about. Not only would this perfect storm have enabled solar and wind energy to mature, but bioenergy, geothermal energy, and wave power would possibly also have grown into competitive technologies. We would most likely also have witnessed a much higher proportion of renewable energy in the pie charts of American energy consumption – and probably also in the rest of the global charts. The American business clusters would have spawned competitors and subsidiaries across the globe. It is possible that Denmark as well as Germany would have been further behind in wind and solar energy. However, it is realistic to assume that the concentration of greenhouse gasses in the atmosphere actually would have been much lower than today. We would still have a climate problem on our hands, but it would be less severe and we would be much better prepared.

THE MISSING LINK

—

The present book is not just a portrait of a number of green heroes. In many ways it is also a portrait of the most overlooked resource in the climate crisis: the individual. In the last decades the enthusiastic men and women who want to share their ideas have disappeared from the debate about global warming. When we contacted innovators around the globe, they responded with surprise – with a few exceptions. They are often lone wolves not used to the limelight, and they do not have a voice in the debate. Just think of newspaper articles and television spots about the climate. What do we tend to see? A politician representing his views or an inventor with a green idea?

The debate is dominated by experts, politicians, and officials, and somewhere in this

"

WE NEED 10,000 INNOVATORS, ALL COLLABORATING WITH, AND BUILDING UPON, ONE ANOTHER TO PRODUCE ALL SORTS OF BREAKTHROUGHS IN ABUNDANT, CLEAN, RELIABLE, AND CHEAP ELECTRONS AND ENERGY EFFICIENCY... ONLY THE MARKET CAN GENERATE AND ALLOCATE ENOUGH CAPITAL FAST ENOUGH AND EFFICIENTLY ENOUGH TO GET 10,000 INVENTORS WORKING IN 10,000 COMPANIES AND 10,000 GARAGES AND 10,000 LABORATORIES TO DRIVE TRANSFORMATIONAL BREAKTHROUGHS; ONLY THE MARKET CAN THEN COMMERCIALIZE THE BEST OF THEM AND IMPROVE ON THE EXISTING ONES AT THE SCOPE, SPEED, AND SCALE WE NEED.

"

Thomas L. Friedman,
"Hot, flat & crowded"
—

Bermuda Triangle the people, whose ideas can make a big difference, disappear. The three dominant voices are deeply concerned with systems and legislation, and none of them support the innovator, even if they are probably all aware that this is wrong. Only in recent years have the corporate leaders, who are the natural spokespersons for innovation, participated in the climate discussions. To a surprising degree, however, they have accepted that systems come before people and have adopted the already existing discourse – thereby also forgetting the human factor.

The result is that the climate equation does not add up. The green heroes are not heard and their conditions are not taken seriously. This may well explain the fact that the pace, with which the solutions are developed, is too slow. As a result it is perplexing to listen to the voices represented in this book. In between beautiful passages about the generation of ideas and die-hard missions it becomes evident that these people actually do what they do *against all odds*. In spite of rules, regulations, economic challenges and adversity. In spite of no support and encouragement.

When waking up in the morning, the first thought in entrepreneur Curtis Felix' mind is how to carry out a project demonstrating his promising algae energy plant at Cape Cod in the North East of the USA. A test will provide the final evidence of whether cold water plankton, as expected, will be able to generate more than 100 times as much bioenergy per square meter as traditional types of energy crops. If that is the case, then Felix will be ready to conquer the market. The local city council and the national defence force have already checked in, wanting to buy his product.

He has just one problem. Money. He needs 20 million dollars in order to carry out the project.

This is not the case with Shi Zhengrong, who is one of China's richest men. His company, Suntech Powers, is among the world's most successful manufacturers of solar cells. Nevertheless, he is up against strong contending forces. The non-polluting energy produced by his solar cells is still expensive compared to coal, oil, and gas, because the competing technologies are free to pump CO_2 into the atmosphere.

In other words: regardless of Shi Zhengrong's personal fortune, the two innovators have one thing in common. To a great extent they create their projects in spite of the framework conditions. If you skim the twenty tales about innovators in this book, it will be crystal clear that we have organized our societies in such a way that they have to put up a brave fight in order to realize their ideas, and that they receive very little help from society, if any at all.

Just think: these people, on whom we all depend for innovation, without whom we will in many ways be lost, should be, knighted, flattered, and celebrated with pomp and circumstance. In actual fact they apply their talents in conditions, which to a great extent prevent them from succeeding. They are running a race, where the hurdles are unnecessarily high.

We can ask ourselves if the great explorations of the fourteenth and the fifteenth centuries would have taken place, if the incentives had been the same as the ones we offer the explorers of our own day and age – the green heroes. Would they have been able to find the passage to India? Would they have discovered that we do not fall over the edge if we sail far

enough towards the East? The comparison is melodramatic, but it somehow makes good sense. As the Indian investment expert and philanthropist Uday Khemka points out, history does not offer many parallels to the green innovators. These people are presently in charge of laying the foundation stones of the paradigms that will ensure that planet Earth in the next decades will be able to sustain 9 billion people and their continued growth and welfare. It is a monstrous task. In many ways it is a journey into the unknown, an almost insane attempt to move boundary lines and explore new frontiers. Just like Vasco da Gama, Sir Francis Drake, and Christopher Columbus set sails on their small, wooden ships and with inaccurate instruments and unskilled crews embarked on voyages to unknown destinations beyond the seven seas.

They did, however, have one thing which many present-day inventors do not: support. The princes and the royal houses of Europe financed their adventures generously, they were considered the most important men in the nation, and when they returned with fantastic tales about unknown continents, they were received with tributes. The heroes of our time are to a great extent living in obscurity until they succeed in getting venture capital or becoming incorporated into a larger company. They are ignored by the media, and the limelight accompanying the environmental prizes, which prefer eloquent experts, loud politicians, and well-meaning chairpersons of various organizations. Many of them are based in humble factory buildings and basements, where they invent their ground-breaking ideas.

They do not whine, but their voices have a touch of bitterness, when you listen to their stories of political failure, infinite rounds of applications and rejected requests for bank loans. If Curtis Felix's application to the authorities for 20 million dollars is turned down this time, he will have to mortgage his house in order to carry on with his project. Otherwise he will have to give up. During our conversation, it becomes evident that he is on the verge of opting for the latter and shelve his dream.

In certain cases the inventors even have to live with ridicule. They are perceived as dreamers. Or "nutcases", As Abasi Musisi from Uganda says. He is the man behind the waste briquettes that save the atmosphere thousands of tons of CO_2 every year.

"Easy is definitely not a word I would use," says Shai Agassi, when referring to the struggle to develop his electric car project Better Place. "When you want to change everything in the car industry and the oil industry in fundamental and aggressive ways, then you are bound to generate resistance. I have learned to accept that. It is an uphill struggle. There are a lot of people, companies, and systems who do not want you to succeed. That is the name of the game, when you want to change a fixed pattern. However: 'you gotta do what you gotta do´.""When you introduce an idea that is environmentally friendly, then you are perceived as a dreamer. People roll their eyes and say: yes, yes. You get the benefit of the doubt, and that is all you get. First you have to prove that your product is for real. Then maybe people will change their minds."

Of course you can laugh at a man who claims he can generate energy by flying kites at an altitude of several kilometers and anchoring them in a turbine, or a woman who makes chairs out of old cardboard tubes. However,

when you consider the haste with which the climate change affect the planet's ecosystems and the enormous technological advances, which we have to master within a few years, you will find that it is no laughing matter. We ought to do our utmost in order to further the inventors' creativity and performance. They should be the most celebrated employees in any company. They should receive the stock options and bonus arrangements that bank managers get. They should be at the top of all charts listing "The World's Most Influential People" and form a queue when the prizes are handed out. Unfortunately the opposite is happening at the moment.

The green inventors are our decade's Bill Gates and his nerd friends who sat in their parent's basements with their bad hair, programming for dear life in the mid 1970s. However, we do not have the funds and the time to wait ten years for the Bill Gateses of the climate age to emerge from their basement labs. We have got to get them into the public eye. We have got to set some goals for their projects, challenge them, encourage them, finance them, build a network of other sharp brains around them and tell them how important their efforts are. The sooner we transform the dreamers into heroes, the better. We must ensure that 20 green heroes today will become 200 next year and 2,000 the following year.

The conversations in this book show that the green heroes are die-hard idealists. They want to make a difference. They want to be part of the solution. In short, there is no doubt that the world leaders need to give them a glimmer of hope. Hope that the world will make up its mind and solve the climate problem. Hope that you can be part of a wider impulse. Hope that our leaders – especially

presidents and prime ministers – will begin to demonstrate leadership and create a global effort here and now. Without this hope it is difficult for the individual to believe that contributing to the big puzzle with just one little piece will make a difference.

Anyone who takes an interest in the climate crisis knows that it can only be solved if we co-operate. There is no "silver bullet", there is no single comprehensive solution, just a swarm of bees, each with their little solution, which in a joint effort will get us to where we want to go.

When you read about the hurdles, which innovators must overcome, then one wonders why they do it. However, the reason is that by and large they are all driven by idealism, by the will to make a difference. But the premise of idealism is hope. Without hope there can be no self-sacrifice, and no altruistic endeavor.

Does it sound like a romantic dream? Perhaps. As we stated in the beginning, However, innovation is not about technology. It is about people. Perhaps we need to realize that establishing the best possible conditions for innovation is not rocket science, but clear, concise choices that influence human creativity. Humanity is the only driving force in world history. In the final analysis it is the individual who takes the community to the next level. Kings, states, and unions create the frameworks, but it is the individual who in a moment of insight conceives the first budding conceptualization of the wheel, the ship, the book, the light bulb, insulin, the airplane, the micro processor, and the sms.
A human being and an idea. That is the missing link we need to place in the centre of climate politics.

TURNING RISK INTO OPPORTUNITY:
THE COPENHAGEN CLIMATE COUNCIL

—

Established in May 2007 by Erik Rasmussen, CEO of Monday Morning - the biggest think tank in Scandinavia - and scientist and author, Tim Flannery, the Copenhagen Climate Council consists of 30 world-renowned business leaders, policy makers, and scientists who have joined forces to create global awareness of the importance of the UN Climate Change Conference (COP15) in Copenhagen in December 2009.

The Council's objective is to establish clear recommendations from international business on the elements needed for a successful new international climate treaty – one that will reduce emissions and safeguard the planet, while promoting economic growth. It seeks to demonstrate that low-carbon businesses can help drive innovation and a transformation of the global economy if government, business and individuals work together.

Promoting green innovation and helping create a supportive framework for new low carbon ideas is key to the Council's - and indeed Monday Morning's – mission.

What sets the Council apart is its diversity in terms of geography and membership, its sole focus on achieving a positive outcome from COP15, and its positive relationship with the Danish government, the host. In addition to convening the World Business Summit on Climate Change, it has, through its Secretariat in Copenhagen, facilitated a number of smaller meetings. In addition, it has written and released a series of thought-provoking essays entitled the *Thought Leadership Series* which have provided inspirational and pro-active guidance on how to combat climate change in innovative new ways.

In June 2008, the Council and the University of California, Berkeley, co-hosted a suc-

MEMBERS OF
THE COPENHAGEN CLIMATE COUNCIL
–

Tim Flannery
Australia / Chairman
Erik Rasmussen
Denmark / CEO /
Monday Morning
Shai Agassi
USA / CEO / Better Place
Carsten Bjerg
Denmark / CEO / Grundfos
David Blood
United Kingdom /
Senior Partner /
Generation Investment
Management LLP
Sir Richard Branson
United Kingdom / CEO /
Virgin Atlantic
James Cameron
United Kingdom /
Vice chairman /
Climate Change Capital
Subhash Chandra
India / CEO /
Zee Entertainment
Jørgen Mads Clausen
Denmark / President &
CEO / Danfoss A/S
Sam DiPiazza, Jr.
USA / CEO /
PriceWaterhouseCoopers
Anders Eldrup
Denmark / CEO / Dong
Energy
Ditlev Engel
Denmark / CEO /
Vestas Wind Systems A/S
Yoichi Funabashi
Japan / Editor-in-Chief /
The Asahi Shimbun
Sultan Al Jaber
Abu Dhabi / CEO /
The Masdar Initiative
Lord Michael Jay
United Kingdom /
Adviser to the Board /
Globe International
Daniel Kammen
USA / Co-Director,
Berkeley Institute of the
Environment /
University of California
Georg Kell
USA / Executive Director /
UN Global Compact
Uday Nabha Khemka
United Kingdom /
Vice Chairman / SUN Group

Sir David King
United Kingdom /
Scientist and Director /
Smith School of Enterprise
and the Environment
Lise Kingo
Denmark / Executive Vice
President, Chief of Staffs /
Novo Nordisk A/S
Dr. Thomas Lovejoy
USA / President / The H.
John Heinz III Center for
Science, Economics and
the Environment
Professor James Lovelock
United Kingdom / Scientist
Rob Morrison
Asia / CEO /
CLSA Asia-Pacific Markets
Robert Purves
Australia /
Chair, boardmember /
Environment Business
Australia,
WWF International
James E Rogers
USA / Chairman,
president & CEO /
Duke Energy Corporation
Zhengrong Shi
People's Republic of China
/ Chairman, CEO / Suntech
Power Holdings Co., Ltd.
Bjørn Stigson
Switzerland / President /
World Business Council
for Sustainable
Development
Sir Crispin Tickell
United Kingdom /
Director /
Oxford University
Moses K. Tsang
Hongkong/ Chairman &
Managing Partner /
Ajia Partners
Jens Ulltveit-Moe
Norway / CEO /
UMOE Group AS
Tracy R. Wolstencroft
USA / Head /
Goldman, Sachs & Co
Ms. Li Xiaolin
People's Republic of China
/ CEO & president /
China Powers
International

cessful science conference on "Innovation in Climate and Energy." The conference explored the science behind new energy supply and demand as well as side technologies developed to help reduce greenhouse emissions.

In May 2009, The Council convened The World Business Summit On Climate Change, the most significant business event on climate change in 2009 with the participation of more than 800 delegates from 48 countries, including more than 500 executives from the private sector.

The output of the World Business Summit on Climate Change was The Copenhagen Call, a powerful message from the global business community to governments. The statement, adopted by the participants at the Summit and developed in partnership with leading organizations such as the World Business Council on Sustainable Development, the World Economic Forum and the Climate Group, is a call for action on climate change with clear recommendations on policy, targets and commitments. Delivered to the Danish Prime Minister Lars Løkke Rasmussen at the conclusion of the Summit on 26 May. the Copenhagen Call is the most significant business statement to decision makers at COP15.

The Council seeks to demonstrate that the climate crisis is not only a huge risk and challenge to humanity, but also a significant opportunity to promote innovative technological solutions and new ventures that will result in a better quality of life for billions of people. It firmly believes that the right solutions to combat climate change will provide the catalyst for new business ventures that will steer us out of a global financial recession.

99

We don't know when we
began doing what we have done.
We do not know what we are doing
right now or how our present actions will
influence the future. What we do know,
however, is that there is only one planet to
do it on, and one species capable of doing
it... Actually we are just at the beginning
of it all. Now we are faced with the
important task of ensuring that we will
never reach the end. And that will
quite likely take a good deal more
than a stroke of luck.

99

Bill Bryson
A Short History of Nearly Everything
—

EPILOGUE

Researching and writing this book has made it even more evident to us that if we are to handle the climate crisis successfully, we must put people first, not systems. Therefore we would like to take the opportunity to thank some of the many unique individuals with whom we have worked during the last three years as a part of the climate program of *Monday Morning*. To a great extent the idea behind the book was generated by this circle of people during the many inspiring conversations we have had about global warming and how to solve the climate crisis.

First of all we should mention the members of the Copenhagen Climate Council, whose names appear in the previous chapter, chairman Tim Flannery, strategic director Nick Rowley and a unique network of partners, among them UN Global Compact, World Business Council for Sustainable Development, World Economic Forums Climate Initiative, The Climate Group, Globe International and Combat Climate Change 3C. They have all made an amazing effort to contribute to the success of the climate summit in Copenhagen.

We have also been very fortunate to have many close dialogues with the hosts of COP15, the Danish government, primarily Climate and Energy Minster Connie Hedegaard, and the hard working team of officials behind her, as well as leading members of the COP15 secretariat in the Ministry of Foreign Affairs and the Prime Minister's office.

It is also a great pleasure to thank Realdania, LEGO, Ingeniørforeningen IDA, and Grontmij Carl Bro, who have supported the PlanetCall project, associated with this book. Thanks are also due to Lone Fredensborg and Jacob Harregaard at the Børsens Forlag. Their expeditious production of this book constitutes a new record.

We are particularly indebted to the employees in the climate team at *Monday Morning* in Copenhagen. Their commitment and professionalism are second to none.

This book is dedicated to the men and women around the globe, who insist on the importance of their green projects and ideas, thereby making it possible for the rest of us to safeguard the planet and create sustainable growth.

Erik Rasmussen
Per Meilstrup
Copenhagen, October 2009

BIBLIO-GRAPHY

—

Writing this book would not have been possible without building on a number of skilled writers, thinkers, scientists, and institutions. It is with great pleasure that we acknowledge their research as our central source of inspiration.

The titles below are among the central works we have consulted:

A Cost Curve for Greenhouse Gas Reduction.
McKinsey & Company (2007)

Breaking the Climate Deadlock. The Climate
Group/The Office of Tony Blair (2008)

***Catalyzing Capital Towards the Low-carbon
Economy.*** Copenhagen Climate Council. David Blood and James Cameron (2009)

***CEO Climate Policy Recommendations to
G8 Leaders.*** World Business Council on Sustainable Development/The World
Economic Forum (2008)

Clear and Present Danger. Steven Chu/UC
Berkeley/Copenhagen Climate Council (2008)

***Climate Change: Global risks, Challenges
& Decisions.*** Copenhagen University (2009).
Synthesis Report from the climate conference
at Copenhagen University in March 2009. The
latest authoritative update of climate science.

Cutting the Cost: The Economic Benefits of Collaborative Climate Ection. The Climate
Group/The Office of Tony Blair (2009)

***Da klimaet blev hot (When climate change
became a hot topic).*** Connie Hedegaard (2008)

The Danish example. Energistyrelsen (2008)

A Short History about Nearly Everything.
Bill Bryson (2005)

Green Jobs and the Clean Energy Economy.
Copenhagen Climate Council.
Daniel M. Kammen and Ditlev Engel (2009)

Pathways to a Low-carbon Economy.
McKinsey & Company (2009)

Stern Review Report on the Economics of Climate Change. Great Britain Treasury (2006)

Strategies for the Green Economy.
Joel Makower (2009)

***Tackling Emissions Growth: The Role of
Markets and Government Regulation.***
Copenhagen Climate Council. Lead author: Samuel A. DiPiazza. Co-authors: James E. Rogers,
Anders Eldrup, Rob Morrison (2008)

Technology for a Low Carbon Future. The
Climate Group/The Office of Tony Blair (2009)

The Business Case for a Strong Global Deal.
Climate Works/Copenhagen Climate
Council (2009)

The CEO's Guide to Climate Action.
Copenhagen Climate Council. Lead author
Samuel A. DiPiazza, Jr. Introduction:
Erik Rasmussen (2008)

The Copenhagen Communiqué.
Corporate Leaders Group (2009)

The Evasive Green Economy.
The Atlantic, Joshua Green (2009)

The Fourth Assessment Report. IPCC (2007).
The UN's climate reports are the authoritative
foundation of the present book on climate
change – and many others. The fourth Assessment report is the latest. The Synthesis Report
provides an excellent overview.

It summarizes the three background reports.
All the material can be downloaded on http://
www.ipcc.ch/

***The Summit Report – The World Business
Summit on Climate Change.***
Copenhagen Climate Council (2009).

World Energy Outlook 2008 and 2009.
International Energy Agency (2008, 2009)

RECOMMENDED READING
In recent years a number of excellent books
have been published, explaining the science
of global warming, the consequences for
nature and humankind, and how we can
meet the challenge. The authors of this book
recommend:

***An Inconvenient Truth: The Planetary
Emergency of Global Warming and What We
Can Do About It.*** Al Gore (2006)

Heat: How to Stop the Planet Burning.
George Monbiot (2006)

Hot, Flat & Crowded.
Thomas L. Friedman (2008)

Now or Never. Tim Flannery (2009)

The Hot Topic. David King and
Gabrielle Walker (2008)

The Revenge of Gaia. James Lovelock (2008)

***The Weathermakers: How Man is Changing
the Climate.*** Tim Flannery (2005)